GRADE

1

Spiral to Infinity Steve Allen

"Fractal images are often made up of small images-within-images, constantly repeating and going smaller and smaller."– **Steve Allen**

Investigations
IN NUMBER, DATA, AND SPACE®

Blocks and Boxes

3-D Geometry

UNIT 9

PEARSON
Scott
Foresman
scottforesman.com

Editorial offices: Glenview, Illinois • Parsippany, New Jersey • New York, New York
Sales offices: Boston, Massachusetts • Duluth, Georgia
Glenview, Illinois • Coppell, Texas • Sacramento, California • Mesa, Arizona

T E R C

The Investigations curriculum was developed by TERC, Cambridge, MA.

NSF

This material is based on work supported by the National Science Foundation ("NSF") under Grant No. ESI-0095450. Any opinions, findings, and conclusions or recommendations expressed in this material are those of the author(s) and do not necessarily reflect the views of the National Science Foundation.

ISBN: 0-328-23734-5

ISBN: 978-0-328-23734-0

7 8 9 10-V003-15 14 13 12 11 10 09 08
CC:N2

TERC

Co-Principal Investigators

Susan Jo Russell

Karen Economopoulos

Authors

Lucy Wittenberg
Director Grades 3–5

Karen Economopoulos
Director Grades K–2

Virginia Bastable
(SummerMath for Teachers,
Mt. Holyoke College)

Katie Hickey Bloomfield

Keith Cochran

Darrell Earnest

Arusha Hollister

Nancy Horowitz

Erin Leidl

Megan Murray

Young Oh

Beth W. Perry

Susan Jo Russell

Deborah Schifter
(Education
Development Center)

Kathy Sillman

Administrative Staff

Amy Taber
Project Manager

Beth Bergeron

Lorraine Brooks

Emi Fujiwara

Contributing Authors

Denise Baumann

Jennifer DiBrienza

Hollee Freeman

Paula Hooper

Jan Mokros

Stephen Monk
(University of Washington)

Mary Beth O'Connor

Judy Storeygard

Cornelia Tierney

Elizabeth Van Cleef

Carol Wright

Technology

Jim Hammerman

Classroom Field Work

Amy Appell

Rachel E. Davis

Traci Higgins

Julia Thompson

Collaborating Teachers

This group of dedicated teachers carried out extensive field testing in their classrooms, met regularly to discuss issues of teaching and learning mathematics, provided feedback to staff, welcomed staff into their classrooms to document students' work, and contributed both suggestions and written material that has been incorporated into the curriculum.

Bethany Altchek

Linda Amaral

Kimberly Beauregard

Barbara Bernard

Nancy Buell

Rose Christiansen

Chris Colbath-Hess

Lisette Colon

Kim Cook

Frances Cooper

Kathleen Drew

Rebeka Eston Salemi

Thomas Fisher

Michael Flynn

Holly Ghazey

Susan Gillis

Danielle Harrington

Elaine Herzog

Francine Hiller

Kirsten Lee Howard

Liliana Klass

Leslie Kramer

Melissa Lee Andrichak

Kelley Lee Sadowski

Jennifer Levitan

Mary Lou LoVecchio

Kristen McEnaney

Maura McGrail

Kathe Millett

Florence Molyneaux

Amy Monkiewicz

Elizabeth Monopoli

Carol Murray

Robyn Musser

Christine Norrman

Deborah O'Brien

Timothy O'Connor

Anne Marie O'Reilly

Mark Paige

Margaret Riddle

Karen Schweitzer

Elisabeth Seyferth

Susan Smith

Debra Sorvillo

Shoshanah Starr

Janice Szymaszek

Karen Tobin

JoAnn Trauschke

Ana Vaisenstein

Yvonne Watson

Michelle Woods

Mary Wright

Note: Unless otherwise noted, all contributors listed above were staff of the Education Research Collaborative at TERC during their work on the curriculum. Other affiliations during the time of development are listed.

Advisors

Deborah Lowenberg Ball,
University of Michigan

Hyman Bass, Professor of Mathematics and Mathematics Education
University of Michigan

Mary Canner, Principal, Natick Public Schools

Thomas Carpenter, Professor of Curriculum and Instruction,
University of Wisconsin-Madison

Janis Freckmann, Elementary Mathematics Coordinator,
Milwaukee Public Schools

Lynne Godfrey, Mathematics Coach,
Cambridge Public Schools

Ginger Hanlon, Instructional Specialist in Mathematics,
New York City Public Schools

DeAnn Huinker, Director, Center for Mathematics and
Science Education Research, University of Wisconsin-Milwaukee

James Kaput, Professor of Mathematics, University of
Massachusetts-Dartmouth

Kate Kline, Associate Professor, Department of Mathematics
and Statistics, Western Michigan University

Jim Lewis, Professor of Mathematics,
University of Nebraska-Lincoln

William McCallum, Professor of Mathematics,
University of Arizona

Harriet Pollatsek, Professor of Mathematics,
Mount Holyoke College

Debra Shein-Gerson, Elementary Mathematics Specialist,
Weston Public Schools

Gary Shevell, Assistant Principal,
New York City Public Schools

Liz Sweeney, Elementary Math Department,
Boston Public Schools

Lucy West, Consultant, Metamorphosis:
Teaching Learning Communities, Inc.

This revision of the curriculum was built on the work of the many authors who contributed to the first edition (published between 1994 and 1998). We acknowledge the critical contributions of these authors in developing the content and pedagogy of *Investigations*:

Authors

Joan Akers

Michael T. Battista

Douglas H. Clements

Karen Economopoulos

Marlene Kliman

Jan Mokros

Megan Murray

Ricardo Nemirovsky

Andee Rubin

Susan Jo Russell

Cornelia Tierney

Contributing Authors

Mary Berle-Carman

Rebecca B. Corwin

Rebeka Eston

Claryce Evans

Anne Goodrow

Cliff Konold

Chris Mainhart

Sue McMillen

Jerrie Moffet

Tracy Noble

Kim O'Neil

Mark Ogonowski

Julie Sarama

Amy Shulman Weinberg

Margie Singer

Virginia Woolley

Tracey Wright

Contents

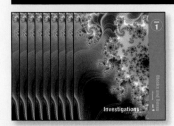

Overview of Program Components

FOR TEACHERS

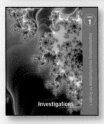

The **Curriculum Units** are the teaching guides. (See far right.)

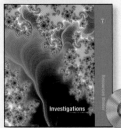

Implementing Investigations in Grade 1 offers suggestions for implementing the curriculum. It also contains a comprehensive index.

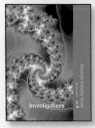

The **Resources Binder** contains all the Resource Masters and Transparencies that support instruction. (Also available on CD) The binder also includes a student software CD.

FOR STUDENTS

The **Student Activity Book** contains the consumable student pages (Recording Sheets, Homework, Practice, and so on).

The **Student Math Handbook** contains Math Words and Ideas pages and Games directions.

The *Investigations* Curriculum

Investigations in Number, Data, and Space® is a K–5 mathematics curriculum designed to engage students in making sense of mathematical ideas. Six major goals guided the development of the *Investigations in Number, Data, and Space®* curriculum. The curriculum is designed to:

- Support students to make sense of mathematics and learn that they can be mathematical thinkers

- Focus on computational fluency with whole numbers as a major goal of the elementary grades

- Provide substantive work in important areas of mathematics—rational numbers, geometry, measurement, data, and early algebra—and connections among them

- Emphasize reasoning about mathematical ideas

- Communicate mathematics content and pedagogy to teachers

- Engage the range of learners in understanding mathematics

Underlying these goals are three guiding principles that are touchstones for the *Investigations* team as we approach both students and teachers as agents of their own learning:

1. *Students have mathematical ideas.* Students come to school with ideas about numbers, shapes, measurements, patterns, and data. If given the opportunity to learn in an environment that stresses making sense of mathematics, students build on the ideas they already have and learn about new mathematics they have never encountered. Students learn that they are capable of having mathematical ideas, applying what they know to new situations, and thinking and reasoning about unfamiliar problems.

2. *Teachers are engaged in ongoing learning* about mathematics content, pedagogy, and student learning. The curriculum provides material for professional development, to be used by teachers individually or in groups, that supports teachers' continued learning as they use the curriculum over several years. The *Investigations* curriculum materials are designed as much to be a dialogue with teachers as to be a core of content for students.

3. *Teachers collaborate with the students and curriculum materials* to create the curriculum as enacted in the classroom. The only way for a good curriculum to be used well is for teachers to be active participants in implementing it. Teachers use the curriculum to maintain a clear, focused, and coherent agenda for mathematics teaching. At the same time, they observe and listen carefully to students, try to understand how they are thinking, and make teaching decisions based on these observations.

Investigations is based on experience from research and practice, including field testing that involved documentation of thousands of hours in classrooms, observations of students, input from teachers, and analysis of student work. As a result, the curriculum addresses the learning needs of real students in a wide range of classrooms and communities. The investigations are carefully designed to invite all students into mathematics—girls and boys; members of diverse cultural, ethnic, and language groups; and students with a wide variety of strengths, needs, and interests.

Based on this extensive classroom testing, the curriculum takes seriously the time students need to develop a strong conceptual foundation and skills based on that foundation. Each curriculum unit focuses on an area of content in depth, providing time for students to develop and practice ideas across a variety of activities and contexts that build on each other. Daily guidelines for time spent on class sessions, Classroom Routines (K–3), and Ten-Minute Math (3–5) reflect the commitment to devoting adequate time to mathematics in each school day.

About This Curriculum Unit

This **Curriculum Unit** is one of nine teaching guides in Grade 1. The ninth unit in Grade 1 is *Blocks and Boxes.*

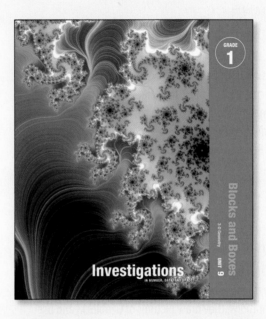

- The **Introduction and Overview** section organizes and presents the instructional materials, provides background information, and highlights important features specific to this unit.

- Each Curriculum Unit contains several **Investigations.** Each Investigation focuses on a set of related mathematical ideas.

- Investigations are divided into one-hour **Sessions,** or lessons.

- Sessions have a combination of these parts: **Activity, Discussion, Math Workshop, Assessment Activity,** and **Session Follow-Up.**

- Each session also has one or more **Classroom Routines** that are done outside of math time.

- At the back of the book is a collection of **Teacher Notes** and **Dialogue Boxes** that provide professional development related to the unit.

- Also included at the back of the book are the **Student Math Handbook** pages for this unit.

- The **Index** provides a way to look up important words or terms.

Overview

OF THIS UNIT

Investigation	Session	Day	
INVESTIGATION 1 **Comparing and Constructing 3-D Shapes** Students comment on the characteristics of Geoblocks and match Geoblock faces to 2-D outlines. They build copies of shapes made from connecting cubes. They also make boxes from various sized rectangles and guess the contents of Mystery Boxes by examining their size and shape.	**1.1** Describing and Comparing Shapes	1	
	1.2 Describing and Comparing Shapes, *continued*	2	
	1.3 Matching Blocks to Pictures	3	
	1.4 Assessment: Blocks in a Sock	4	
	1.5 Assessment: Matching Blocks to Outlines	5	
	1.6 What Kind of Box Is It?	6	
	1.7 Making Boxes	7	
	1.8 Revealing the Mystery Boxes	8	
INVESTIGATION 2 **Building a Block Town** As students move back and forth between 2-D and 3-D representations, they draw pictures of Geoblocks and use plans to make Geoblock buildings. The class builds a Block Town on a large grid, and students give directions from one location to another using a combination of turns and steps.	**2.1** Drawing Geoblocks	9	
	2.2 Building from a Plan	10	
	2.3 Buildings for Our Town	11	
	2.4 Building Our Town	12	
	2.5 Building Our Town, *continued*	13	
	2.6 Giving Directions	14	
	2.7 Giving Directions, *continued*	15	
	2.8 End-of-Unit Assessment	16	

Each *Investigations* session has some combination of these five parts: **Activity, Discussion, Math Workshop, Assessment Activity,** and **Session Follow-Up.** These session parts are indicated in the chart below. Each session also has one or more **Classroom Routines** that are done outside of math time.

Activity	Discussion	Math Workshop	Assessment Activity	Session Follow-Up
●●		●		●
●●		●		●
●	●●			●
●		●	●	●
	●	●	●	●
●●●				●
●	●			●
●	●			●
●●	●			●
●●	●			●
●	●●			●
●		●		●
	●	●		●
●●●				●
●		●		●
			●	●

Classroom Routines

Quick Images	Morning Meeting	Quick Survey	Tell a Story
●			
		●	
			●
●			
		●	
			●
	●		
		●	
			●
	●		
		●	
			●
●			
		●	
			●
	●		

Mathematics

IN THIS UNIT

Blocks and Boxes is the last of nine units in the Grade 1 sequence and the second of two units in the Grade 1 geometry strand. These units develop ideas about 2-D and 3-D shapes and the relationship between them—their characteristics and attributes, how to compose and decompose them in different ways, and how to sort, categorize, and name them. The mathematical focus of this unit is on: observing, describing, comparing, and building 3-D shapes; developing vocabulary for naming and describing 2-D and 3-D shapes; and exploring the relationship between 2-D and 3-D shapes.

Students match Geoblocks to 2-D outlines of their faces, to pictures, and to drawings. They investigate rectangular prisms, including boxes that they collect and boxes that they construct from different-sized rectangles. They make their own drawings of Geoblock buildings and plan and construct a town made from Geoblocks. Students also work with directions and paths as they plan routes through their town.

 In Kindergarten, students began to observe, describe, compare, and represent the shapes they see around them. In their first geometry unit, students observed, described, compared, sorted, classified, represented, and built with 2-D shapes. The focus of this work was on the characteristics of a variety of 2-D shapes—particularly triangles—and the relationships among these shapes. Students used pattern blocks and the *Shapes* software to put together shapes and to make patterns and designs. They used Shape Cards to sort and describe groups of shapes. As they worked with these materials, they learned about the characteristics of a variety of 2-D shapes and the relationships among these shapes.

In this unit, students' work focuses on three mathematical emphases:

1 Features of Shape Describing and comparing 2-D and 3-D shapes

Math Focus Points

- Developing vocabulary to describe 3-D shapes and their attributes
- Comparing size, shape, and orientation of objects
- Identifying the characteristics of 3-D objects by touch
- Describing a rectangular prism
- Comparing rectangular prisms
- Observing and describing characteristics of 3-D shapes
- Recognizing shapes in the world
- Describing 3-D structures

Students experience geometry every day; shapes, angles, motions, and patterns are everywhere in a child's world. Part of students' mathematical work is to begin to observe, describe, compare, and represent the shapes they see around them. Therefore, this unit emphasizes careful observation, description, and comparison of 3-D shapes. Students look for shapes in their own environment, and they work with 3-D shapes such as Geoblocks, manufactured boxes, and boxes made by students (all of which have familiar 2-D shapes as their faces).

Another emphasis of this unit is how shapes can go together or be taken apart to make other shapes. Students have been exploring composition and decomposition in the following contexts all year:

- Ten can be broken up into 5 and 5 or into 6 and 4.
- A hexagon can be made with one pattern block hexagon or with six pattern block triangles.

In this unit, students become familiar with the following equivalencies in the Geoblock set:

- Two cubes can be put together to make one rectangular prism.
- Two triangular prisms can be put together to make one cube.

This work makes students more aware of relationships among shapes.

2 Features of Shape Exploring the relationships between 2-D and 3-D shapes

Math Focus Points

- Matching a 3-D object to a 2-D outline of one of its faces
- Matching a 3-D object to a 2-D picture of the object
- Making 3-D objects out of 2-D pieces
- Making a 2-D representation of a 3-D object or structure
- Building a 3-D construction from a 2-D representation

Students also investigate the relationship between 3-D shapes and 2-D representations of those shapes. Through matching 3-D objects to their outlines, pictures, and drawings, they learn about identifying shapes by looking carefully at some parts of the shapes and then visualizing what the whole shapes must look like. When students draw their own representations of 3-D blocks and buildings, they have to pay attention to the parts of these shapes and how they are put together. As students draw their buildings, they are encouraged to think carefully about the shapes and relative sizes of the blocks. By constructing their own boxes from different sizes of rectangles, they explore how a rectangular prism (a box shape) is made of pairs of congruent rectangles that form the opposite sides of the prism.

Moving back and forth between 3-D objects and 2-D representations helps students describe and compare the characteristics of common 3-D shapes.

This Unit also focuses on

- Relating the size and shape of an object to its use
- Planning a geometric structure with limited space and materials
- Visualizing and estimating the paces and turns required to follow a particular path
- Giving, following, and recording directions for following a path
- Counting and adding to compare the distances of different paths

Classroom Routines focus on

- Developing strategies for counting accurately
- Using the calendar as a tool for keeping track of time
- Developing vocabulary to talk about time (*morning, noon, midday, afternoon,* and so on) and sequence (*first, next, last, before, after,* and so on)
- Collecting and recording data
- Counting, describing, and comparing data
- Estimating quantities up to about 30
- Adding or subtracting small amounts to/from a familiar number
- Investigating numbers that can (and cannot) be made into groups of two
- Making sense of a variety of representations of data
- Naming and telling time to the hour on digital and analog clocks
- Associating times on the hour with daily events
- Developing visual images of, and language for describing, 2-D shapes
- Identifying names and attributes of 2-D shapes
- Collecting, counting, representing, describing, and comparing data
- Interpreting different representations of data, including pictures, bar graphs, tallies, and Venn diagrams
- Connecting standard notation ($+$, $-$, $=$) to the actions and relationships they represent
- Creating a story problem for a given expression
- Developing strategies for adding and subtracting small numbers
- Solving related problems

LOOKING FORWARD

In this unit, students look carefully at 3-D shapes—and the 2-D shapes that make up their faces—and spend time describing, comparing, constructing, and representing them. This lays the foundation for work students will do in the geometry units in Grades 2, 3, and beyond. They will look at many examples of a shape (e.g., various rectangles or rectangular prisms), and they will sort and categorize a variety of 2-D and 3-D shapes according to specific attributes (e.g., the number of sides or the size of angles). The work in this unit will also support students when they revisit and deepen their understanding of the relationships between 2-D and 3-D shapes, paths, distance, locations in space, and giving directions through space.

Assessment

I N   T H I S   U N I T

ONGOING ASSESSMENT: Observing Students at Work

The following sessions provide **Ongoing Assessment: Observing Students at Work** opportunities:

- **Session 1.1, pp. 24, 26, and 27**
- **Session 1.2, p. 31**
- **Session 1.3, p. 36**
- **Session 1.4, p. 42**
- **Session 1.5, p. 45**

- **Session 1.6, p. 54**
- **Session 2.1, pp. 70 and 72**
- **Session 2.2, p. 76**
- **Session 2.3, p. 82**

- **Session 2.4, pp. 86 and 87**
- **Session 2.6, p. 98**
- **Session 2.7, p. 101**
- **Session 2.8, p. 105**

WRITING OPPORTUNITIES

The following sessions have **writing** opportunities for students to explain their mathematical thinking:

- **Session 1.5, p. 48**
  Student Activity Book, p. 10

- **Session 2.4, p. 85**
  M24, Describing My Building

- **Session 2.7, p. 102**
  Student Activity Book, p. 29

- **Session 2.1, p. 73**
  Student Activity Book, p. 15

PORTFOLIO OPPORTUNITIES

The following sessions have work appropriate for a **portfolio:**

- **Session 1.5, p. 45**
  M19, Assessment: Matching Blocks
  to Outlines

- **Session 2.7, p. 100**
  Student Activity Book, pp. 24–25

- **Session 2.8, p. 104**
  M26, End-of-Unit Assessment:
  Matching Plans to Buildings

- **Session 2.4, p. 85**
  M24, Describing My Building

Assessing the Benchmarks

Observing students as they engage in conversation about their ideas is a primary means to assess their mathematical understanding. Consider all of your students' work, not just the written assessments. See the chart below for suggestions about key activities to observe.

 Checklist Available

Benchmarks in This Unit	Key Activities to Observe	Assessment
1. Attend to features of 3-D shapes, such as overall size and shape, the number and shape of faces, and the number of corners.	**Sessions 1.4, 1.5:** Blocks in a Sock	**Sessions 1.4, 1.5:** Assessment Activity: Blocks in a Sock ✓
2. Match a 2-D representation to a 3-D shape or structure.	**Sessions 1.1, 1.2, 1.4, 1.5:** Geoblock Footprints **Sessions 2.1, 2.2:** Building and Drawing **Session 2.2:** Building from Pictures	**Session 1.5:** Assessment Activity: Matching Blocks to Outlines **Session 2.8:** End-of-Unit Assessment: Matching Plans to Buildings

Relating the Mathematical Emphases to the Benchmarks

Mathematical Emphases	Benchmarks
Features of Shape Describing and comparing 2-D and 3-D shapes	1
Features of Shape Exploring the relationships between 2-D and 3-D shapes	2

Classroom Routines

Classroom Routines offer practice and review of key concepts for this grade level. These daily activities, to be done in ten minutes outside of math class, occur in a regular rotation every 4–5 days. Specific directions for the day's routine are provided in each session. For the full description and variations of each classroom routine see *Implementing Investigations in Grade 1.*

Morning Meeting

Students continue to use the calendar to keep track of time and events, collect and analyze data about the weather, and count the number of students in the class. Variations focus on solving problems based on the calendar and the number of students in class and on telling time.

Math Focus Points

◆ Developing strategies for counting accurately

◆ Using the calendar as a tool for keeping track of time

◆ Developing vocabulary to talk about time (*morning, noon, midday, afternoon,* and so on) and sequence (*first, next, last, before, after,* and so on)

◆ Collecting and recording data

◆ Counting, describing, and comparing data

◆ Estimating quantities up to about 30

◆ Adding or subtracting small amounts to/from a familiar number

◆ Investigating numbers that can (and cannot) be made into groups of two

◆ Making sense of a variety of representations of data

◆ Naming and telling time to the hour on digital and analog clocks

◆ Associating times on the hour with daily events

Quick Images

Students draw and compare various shapes.

Math Focus Points

◆ Developing visual images of, and language for describing, 2-D shapes

◆ Identifying names and attributes of 2-D shapes

Quick Survey

Students collect, organize, record, and discuss data about the class.

Math Focus Points

◆ Collecting, counting, representing, describing, and comparing data

◆ Interpreting different representations of data, including pictures, bar graphs, tallies, and Venn diagrams

Tell a Story

Students generate a story problem for a given addition or subtraction equation.

Math Focus Points

◆ Connecting standard notation ($+$, $-$, $=$) to the actions and relationships they represent

◆ Creating a story problem for a given expression

◆ Developing strategies for adding and subtracting small numbers

◆ Solving related problems

Practice and Review

IN THIS UNIT

Practice and review play a critical role in the *Investigations* program. The following components and features are available to provide regular reinforcement of key mathematical concepts and procedures.

Books	Features	In This Unit . . .
Curriculum Unit	**Classroom Routines** offer practice and review of key concepts for this grade level. These daily activities, to be done in ten minutes outside of math class, occur in a regular rotation every 4–5 days. Specific directions for the day's routine are provided in each session. For the full description and variations of each classroom routine see *Implementing Investigations in Grade 1.*	• **All sessions**
Student Activity Book	**Daily Practice** pages in the *Student Activity Book* provide one of three types of written practice: **reinforcement** of the content of the unit, **ongoing review,** or **enrichment** opportunities. Some Daily Practice pages will also have Ongoing Review items with multiple-choice problems similar to those on standardized tests.	• **All sessions**
	Homework pages in the *Student Activity Book* are an extension of the work done in class. At times they help students prepare for upcoming activities.	• **Session 1.2** • **Session 1.3** • **Session 1.4** • **Session 1.5** • **Session 2.1** • **Session 2.5** • **Session 2.7**
Student Math Handbook	**Math Words and Ideas** in the *Student Math Handbook* are pages that summarize key words and ideas. Most Words and Ideas pages have at least one exercise.	• **Student Math Handbook, pp. 83–92**
	Games pages are found in a section of the *Student Math Handbook.*	• **No games are introduced in this unit.**

Differentiation

Supporting the Range of Learners

Sessions	1.1	1.2	1.3	1.4	1.5	1.6	1.7	1.8	2.1	2.2	2.3	2.6	2.7
Intervention	•		•	•	•	•			•	•	•		•
Extension	•	•		•		•	•	•	•				•
ELL		•	•								•	•	

Intervention

Suggestions are made to support and engage students who are having difficulty with a particular idea, activity, or problem.

Extension

Suggestions are made to support and engage students who finish early or may be ready for additional challenge.

English Language Learners (ELL)

To take part in many of this unit's activities, students must be familiar with words that are commonly used to describe shapes. You can support English Language Learners by helping them develop this vocabulary. Examine a set of Geoblocks together, and encourage students to say what they notice about them. Record the words they use on a vocabulary chart. As students share words (e.g., *round, square, pointy, flat, big, small, skinny,* and *wide*) have English Language Learners look for other Geoblocks that can be described with the same terms. Draw pictures to illustrate the words. Encourage students to refer to the chart during class discussions and other activities. In addition, remind students to refer to the Math Words and Ideas pages in the *Student Math Handbook.*

In this unit's final sessions, students must use directional terminology such as *right, left, straight,* and *forward;* they must also understand the words *north, south, east,* and *west.* You can reinforce this vocabulary by having English Language Learners identify various locations on a sketched map of your classroom. Post the map on the wall and ask questions such as What's to the *right* of the blackboard? What's to the *left* of the bookcases? If I took 10 steps *forward* from my chair on the reading rug, where would I be? Then have students take turns asking each other questions about the map. If time permits, you can label the sides of the map *north, south, east,* and *west* and practice using those terms as well.

Working with the Range of Learners: Classroom Cases is a set of episodes written by teachers that focuses on meeting the needs of the range of learners in the classroom. In the first section, *Setting up the Mathematical Community,* teachers write about how they create a supportive and productive learning environment in their classrooms. In the next section, *Accommodations for Learning,* teachers focus on specific modifications they make to meet the needs of some of their learners. In the last section, *Language and Representation,* teachers share how they help students use representations and develop language to investigate and express mathematical ideas. The questions at the end of each case provide a starting point for your own reflection or for discussion with colleagues. See *Implementing Investigations in Grade 1* for this set of episodes.

Mathematical Emphases

Features of Shape Describing and comparing 2-D and 3-D shapes

Math Focus Points

◆ Developing vocabulary to describe 3-D shapes and their attributes

◆ Comparing size, shape, and orientation of objects

◆ Identifying the characteristics of 3-D objects by touch

◆ Describing a rectangular prism

◆ Comparing rectangular prisms

Features of Shape Exploring the relationships between 2-D and 3-D shapes

Math Focus Points

◆ Matching a 3-D object to a 2-D outline of one of its faces

◆ Matching a 3-D object to a 2-D picture of the object

◆ Making 3-D objects out of 2-D pieces

This Investigation also focuses on

◆ Relating the size and shape of an object to its use

Comparing and Constructing 3-D Shapes

	Student Activity Book	Student Math Handbook	Professional Development: Read Ahead of Time	
SESSION 1.1 p. 22				
Describing and Comparing Shapes Students develop language for describing 3-D shapes as they comment on the characteristics of Geoblocks. They attend to features of 3-D shapes as they build copies of shapes from connecting cubes and match 3-D Geoblocks to 2-D outlines of Geoblock faces.	1	83, 85, 86, 90	• **Mathematics in This Unit**, p. 10 • **Teacher Note:** Types of 3-D Shapes, p. 107 • **Dialogue Box:** It Reminds Me Of . . . , p. 116	
SESSION 1.2 p. 29				
Describing and Comparing Shapes, *continued* Students continue building copies of Cube Things and matching Geoblocks to outlines of their faces. Class discussion focuses on describing and comparing Geoblocks.	2–3	83, 85, 86, 90		
SESSION 1.3 p. 33				
Matching Blocks to Pictures Students try to determine the identity of a mystery object, given its 2-D outline (or footprint). Then, they work to match 2-D pictures of Geoblocks to actual blocks. Class discussion focuses on strategies for matching 2-D representations to 3-D objects.	3, 5	83, 85, 86, 89, 90	• **Dialogue Box:** Comparing Blocks to Pictures, p. 117	
SESSION 1.4 p. 39				
Assessment: Blocks in a Sock Students play Blocks in a Sock, using tactile information to try to identify a 3-D shape. Math Workshop continues to focus on exploring the characteristics of Geoblocks and replicating constructions made with connecting cubes.	6–8	83, 88, 90		

Classroom Routines See page 14 for an overview.

Morning Meeting	Quick Survey
• A daily classroom schedule with the time of events posted in both analog and digital representations.	• *Quick Survey* charts for sessions 1.2, 1.5, and 1.8. See instructions on pages 29, 44, and 60.
Quick Images	**Tell a Story**
• T61–T63, Shape Cards 🖨 Cut out images and store in envelope	• Chart paper

Materials to Gather	Materials to Prepare
• **Connecting cubes** (10 per student)	• **Geoblocks** Divide 2 sets of Geoblocks into 4 equal subsets for distribution around the class. As you do so, familiarize yourself with the shapes and their names. • **M1–M2, Geoblock Footprints: Sets A and B** Familiarize yourself with the Geoblocks that fit the footprints on each set and make copies. (6–8 of each set) • **M3–M4, Family Letter** Make copies. (1 per student) • **Cube Things** Make 4 or 5 identically shaped Cube Things, each with 8–10 connecting cubes. Cube colors can vary.
• **Materials for Geoblock Footprints** See Session 1.1. • **Materials for Copying Cube Things** See Session 1.1. • **Geoblocks** (4 subsets; including Geoblock K)	• **M5, Geoblock Footprints: Set C** Familiarize yourself with the Geoblocks that fit the footprints on this sheet and make copies. (6–8; optional)
• **T64, Geoblock Pictures: Sheet A** 🖨 • **T65, Geoblock Pictures: Sheet C** 🖨 • **Self-stick notes** (as needed) • **Geoblocks** (2 subsets) • **Extra paper for wrapping** (as needed)	• **M9–M12, Geoblock Pictures: Sheets A–D** Make copies. (1 of each per pair; plus 1 extra) • **M13, Boxes for Our Collection** Make copies. (1 per student) • **Sample Mystery Box** Find a small, empty box. Write on it what it used to hold and wrap it in brown paper. (optional)
• **M9–M12, Geoblock Pictures: Sheets A–D** (1 of each per every 3 pairs; from Session 1.3) • **Geoblocks J and P** • **Materials for Build a Wall** See Session 1.2. • **Materials for Geoblock Footprints** See Session 1.1. • **Materials for Copying Cube Things** See Session 1.1.	• **M14, Assessment Checklist: Observing Blocks in a Sock** ☑ Make copies. (2 or 3) • **M15–M18, Geoblock Footprints: Sets D–G** Make copies. (1 of each per pair)

🖨 Overhead Transparency   ☑ Checklist Available

Comparing and Constructing 3-D Shapes, *continued*

	Student Activity Book	Student Math Handbook	Professional Development: Read Ahead of Time	
SESSION 1.5 p. 44				
Assessment: Matching Blocks to Outlines As an assessment, students work individually to match pictures of Geoblocks to outlines of their faces. Math Workshop continues to focus on exploring the characteristics of Geoblocks and of things made with connecting cubes. Class discussion focuses on strategies for finding blocks that match pictures and finding blocks by feel.	9–10	83, 88, 90	• **Teacher Note:** Assessment: Matching Blocks to Outlines, p. 109	
SESSION 1.6 p. 49				
What Kind of Box Is It? As a class, students look at some of the Mystery Boxes they bring from home and talk about what kind of boxes they think these could be and why. A discussion about the characteristics of boxes—including the number of faces—serves as an introduction to students constructing their own 3-D boxes from rectangular 2-D pieces.	11	86, 87	• **Teacher Notes:** Types of 3-D Shapes, p. 107; Students Make Their Own Boxes, p. 111	
SESSION 1.7 p. 56				
Making Boxes Students continue making 3-D boxes from 2-D shapes. Class discussion focuses on comparing the boxes students have made.	12	85, 86, 87		
SESSION 1.8 p. 60				
Revealing the Mystery Boxes Students finish making 3-D boxes from 2-D shapes. Class discussion focuses on what students think some of the Mystery Boxes hold and why. Then, some are revealed.	13	85, 86, 87	• **Dialogue Box:** Baby Shoes and Birdhouses, p. 119	

Materials to Gather	Materials to Prepare
• **Materials for Blocks in a Sock** See Session 1.4. • **Materials for Build a Wall** See Session 1.2. • **Materials for Geoblock Footprints** See Session 1.1. • **Materials for Copying Cube Things** See Session 1.4. • **T66, Geoblock Pictures: Set D** • **Geoblocks S, V, C, O, U, X, J, and G** (as needed) • **Geoblocks R, O, S, M, P, C, Q, N, and T**	• **M19, Assessment: Matching Blocks to Outlines** Make copies. (1 per student)
• **Blank pieces of paper or large index cards** (optional) • **Clear or masking tape** (1 per pair) • **Scissors** (1 per every 3 or 4 students) • **Connecting cubes** (class set) • **Envelopes** (1 per pair)	• **Mystery Box Collection** Supplement students' Mystery Box display as needed with unusual shapes, such as an oatmeal box or candy bar boxes shaped like triangular prisms. • **Box Pieces: Set A** Gather seven 3″ x 5″ cards and four 5″ x 8″ cards per pair. See cutting instructions, Session 1.6, page 52. (1 set per pair) • **Demonstration box** Create 1 box from the materials in 1 envelope of Box Pieces: Set A. • **Collection of small objects** Collect small objects for students to make boxes for, such as pencils of different lengths, crayons, shells, small cars, figurines, and so on.
• **Materials for Making Boxes with Cards** See Session 1.6. • **Students' boxes** (from Session 1.6)	• **Box Pieces: Set B** Gather one to three sets of eighteen 3″ x 5″ cards and eight 5″ x 8″ cards. See cutting instructions, Session 1.7, page 57.
• **Materials for Making Boxes with Cards** See Sessions 1.6 and 1.7. • **Index cards** (as needed) • **Collection of Mystery Boxes** (from Session 1.6)	

Overhead Transparency   ✓ Checklist Available

Describing and Comparing Shapes

Math Focus Points

◆ Developing vocabulary to describe 3-D shapes and their attributes

◆ Comparing size, shape, and orientation of objects

◆ Matching a 3-D object to a 2-D outline of one of its faces

Vocabulary

geometry
footprint

Today's Plan		Materials
① ACTIVITY **Describing Geoblocks**	10 MIN CLASS	• Geoblocks*
② ACTIVITY **Introducing Geoblock Footprints and Copying Cube Things**	10 MIN CLASS	• M1* • Geoblocks; Cube Thing*
③ MATH WORKSHOP **Building and Matching 3-D Shapes** **③A** Geoblock Footprints **③B** Copying Cube Things	40 MIN	**3A** • M1–M2* • Geoblocks **3B** • Cube Things*; connecting cubes
④ SESSION FOLLOW-UP **Daily Practice**		• *Student Activity Book*, p. 1 • M3–M4, Family Letter* • *Student Math Handbook*, pp. 83, 85, 86, 90

*See *Materials to Prepare,* p. 19.

Classroom Routines

Quick Images: Shapes Show transparencies from Shape Cards (T61–T63), beginning with Shape B. Follow the basic *Quick Images* activity. Ask students to describe the shape after it has been drawn. Repeat with Shape D and then with Shape O. Compare the three shapes at the end of the activity.

ACTIVITY

1 Describing Geoblocks

10 MIN   CLASS

Explain that today the class is beginning a new unit on geometry and that for the next few weeks you will be looking closely at many different shapes.

Hold up one of the larger Geoblock cubes so that everyone can see. ❶

Geoblock D

What is one thing you can say about this block?

It's like a box. What else can you say? It's smooth. It has corners. It has squares.

As students share, point out (or have students point out) the various attributes of your block. ❷

After students have described the shape, choose one description that distinguishes it from some of the other shapes in the Geoblock set. ❸

You said that this shape looks like a box. Look in the Geoblock set near you and find another block that you think looks like a box. It doesn't have to be exactly the same as this one, as long as it looks like a box.

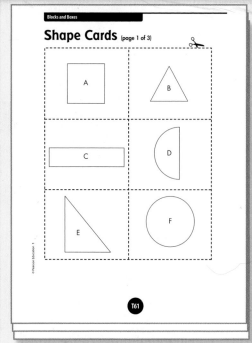

Blocks and Boxes

Shape Cards (page 1 of 3)

T61

▲ **Transparencies, T61–T63**

Teaching Note

❶ **Exploring Geoblocks** Students should be familiar with Geoblocks from their experience in How Many of Each? If students have not used Geoblocks recently, they may need time to explore them to learn about their characteristics and discover the relationships among the shapes. Such exploration gives students the chance to pursue their own ideas so that later on they can turn their attention to the specific tasks you set for them. Include free exploration with Geoblocks as a Math Workshop activity in this investigation as needed.

Professional Development

❷ **Dialogue Box:** It Reminds Me Of. . . , p. 116

❸ **Teacher Note:** Types of 3-D Shapes, p. 107

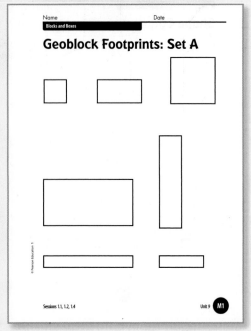

▲ Resource Masters, M1

The panel above (Resource Masters, M1) contains:

Name _____ Date _____

Blocks and Boxes

Geoblock Footprints: Set A

Sessions 1.1, 1.2, 1.4   Unit 9 **M1**

ONGOING ASSESSMENT: Observing Students at Work

Students consider the characteristics of 3-D shapes and look for blocks with a given attribute.

- **What blocks do students choose?** Do they look for an exact match or a cube of any size? Do some choose other box shapes, such as rectangular prisms? Do any students have trouble finding a block that matches the description?

Repeat this process with a triangular prism from the Geoblock set.

Geoblock R

Show students the block and ask them to describe it. Then, using students' words, discuss one of the characteristics that they mention.

[Marta] said that this block is pointy. Find a block in your set that you think is pointy.

[Felipe], can you show us why you think your block is pointy?

ACTIVITY

🕙 10 MIN   👥 CLASS

2 Introducing Geoblock Footprints and Copying Cube Things

To introduce Geoblock Footprints, show students Geoblock Footprints: Set A (M1).

The shapes on this page are footprints of some of the Geoblocks. For this Math Workshop Activity, your job is to find a block that fits on each footprint exactly.

Students match the Geoblocks to their footprints for this activity.

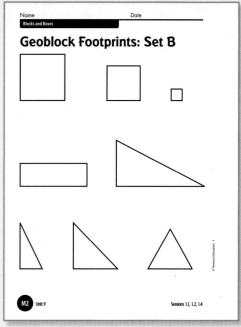

▲ Resource Masters, M2

Demonstrate by placing one of the Geoblocks on the footprint. Emphasize that the challenge is to find one block that fills the whole footprint and not to find combinations of blocks that fill the outline.

When you find a match, place the block directly on the matching outline and leave it there until you have filled the whole sheet. You should end up with seven blocks on the sheet for Set A.

Students may use seven different blocks, or they may use the same type of block more than once. They should work on both Geoblock Footprints: Sets A and B (M1–M2).

To introduce Copying Cube Things, show students the Cube Thing you made with 8–10 cubes.

For this Math Workshop activity, your job will be to make an exact match of this Cube Thing. You don't have to match the colors, just the shape.

Tell students that they will work in pairs for this activity. After they copy the Cube Things you made, and have checked each other's work, they can make their own Cube Things to copy. One student will use a maximum of ten cubes to make a Cube Thing that the partner will copy. If the copy does not match the original, the pair will make adjustments as needed.

Math Note

4 Footprints on Sets A and B Many different blocks will fit each shape on Geoblock Footprints: Set A (M1). There is only one Geoblock to match some of the shapes on Geoblocks Footprints: Set B (M2), but the shapes are quite distinctive. Spend some time before class finding blocks that fit the footprints.

MATH WORKSHOP

3 Building and Matching 3-D Shapes

40 MIN

Explain that students will be working on Geoblock Footprints and copying Cube Things for the rest of this session and most of the next session. During this Math Workshop, students should spend some time working on both activities.

3A Geoblock Footprints

PAIRS

For complete details about Geoblock Footprints, see the previous activity and consider the following notes.4

ONGOING ASSESSMENT: Observing Students at Work

Students find blocks with faces that match a given footprint or outline.

- **How do students find blocks that match the given outlines?** Which footprints do they find difficult? Do they keep in mind all the shapes on the sheet as they work? For example, when a shape does not match one outline, do they check to see whether it matches any of the others?

- **Can students differentiate between different sizes of the same shape?** Do they recognize differences among squares, triangles, and rectangles that are not squares? Do they notice that the triangular prisms have some rectangular faces, even though the overall shape seems to be triangular?

- **What language do students use to describe these shapes?**

Students work on Geoblock Footprints.

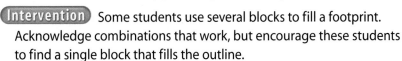

DIFFERENTIATION: Supporting the Range of Learners

Intervention Some students use several blocks to fill a footprint. Acknowledge combinations that work, but encourage these students to find a single block that fills the outline.

Intervention If students cannot find all the shapes on a sheet and become frustrated, encourage them to put that sheet with the blocks that they have found so far aside and to try the next sheet. You may also hint that rectangles can be "hiding" within triangular-looking shapes.

Extension Students ready for more of a challenge can try to use all different blocks to fill each sheet.

3B Copying Cube Things

PAIRS

For complete details about Copying Cube Things, see the previous activity, and consider the following notes.

ONGOING ASSESSMENT: Observing Students at Work

Students build an exact replica of a given 3-D object.

- **How do students approach the task?** Do they mentally or visually break the Cube Thing into parts? Do they count the cubes in each part? Do they directly compare the parts?

- **Can students tell whether their Cube Thing matches the original?** Do they adjust their work if it does not? Whether or not all the details are exactly right, do students build a Cube Thing that matches the general size and shape of the original?

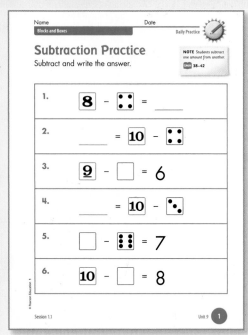

Subtraction Practice
Subtract and write the answer.

NOTE Students subtract one amount from another. SMH 38–42

1. **8** − ⚁ = _____

2. _____ = **10** − ⚃

3. **9** − ☐ = 6

4. _____ = **10** − ⚂

5. ☐ − ⚅ = 7

6. **10** − ☐ = 8

Session 1.1   Unit 9 ①

▲ Student Activity Book, p. 1

DIFFERENTIATION: Supporting the Range of Learners

Intervention Help students who have trouble making an exact copy of a Cube Thing focus on the different parts that make up the whole.

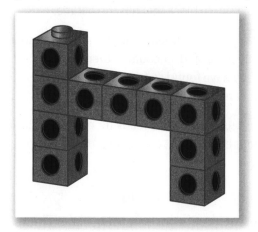

You said that my Cube Thing looks like a chair. How many cubes are in the front leg? Can you make that part of your chair?

Let's compare them. [Place the Cube Things side by side.] Are they the same? What about the seat of the chair—the part that goes across?

4 SESSION FOLLOW-UP
Daily Practice

Daily Practice: For ongoing review, have students complete *Student Activity Book* page 1.

Student Math Handbook: Students and families may use *Student Math Handbook* pages 83, 85, 86, 90 for reference and review. See pages 124–126 in the back of this unit.

Family Letter: Send home copies of the Family Letter (M3– M4).

Describing and Comparing Shapes, *continued*

Math Focus Points

◆ Developing vocabulary to describe 3-D shapes and their attributes

◆ Comparing size, shape, and orientation of objects

◆ Matching a 3-D object to a 2-D outline of one of its faces

Vocabulary
face

Today's Plan		Materials
ACTIVITY **①** **Introducing Build a Wall** 5 MIN · CLASS		• Geoblock K; Geoblocks
MATH WORKSHOP **②** **Building and Matching 3-D Shapes** **2A** Build a Wall **2B** Geoblock Footprints **2C** Copying Cube Things 45 MIN		**2A** • Geoblocks **2B** • Materials from Session 1.1, p. 22 **2C** • Materials from Session 1.1, p. 22
ACTIVITY **③** **Describing Geoblocks** 10 MIN · CLASS		• Geoblocks
SESSION FOLLOW-UP **④** **Daily Practice and Homework**		• *Student Activity Book,* pp. 2–3 • *Student Math Handbook,* pp. 83, 85, 86, 90

*See *Materials to Prepare,* p. 19.

Classroom Routines

Quick Survey: More Buttons or Zippers? On chart paper, create a horizontal table with two rows titled "Are you wearing more buttons or more zippers?" Label the top row "Buttons" and the bottom row "Zippers." Use checkmarks (✓) to record students' responses and then count them. If students do not make the observation, note how the number of checkmarks is the same as the number of students in the class.

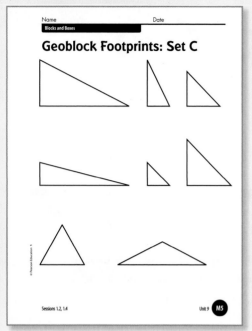

▲ **Resource Masters, M5**

ACTIVITY

1 Introducing Build a Wall

5 MIN CLASS

Show students Geoblock K and briefly explain the activity.

For this activity, you are going to build a wall that's the same shape as this block. Think of this block as the first block in the wall. Your job is to continue building the wall with any blocks from the set, to keep the wall the same height and thickness.

Encourage students to use a variety of types of blocks without showing them too many examples so that they will be challenged during Math Workshop.

MATH WORKSHOP

2 Building and Matching 3-D Shapes

45 MIN

Students choose among the following activities: Build a Wall, Geoblock Footprints, and Copying Cube Things. Build a Wall is a structured activity that can be helpful for students who need more experience with the Geoblocks.

2A Build a Wall

PAIRS

Students make Geoblock K the first block of a wall and then continue the wall, using any blocks from the set.

ONGOING ASSESSMENT: Observing Students at Work

Students build a wall that is the same height and thickness as a given Geoblock.

- **How do students find the Geoblocks needed to build the wall?**
  Do they use a variety of different kinds of blocks or do they think that only cubes and/or rectangular prisms will work?

DIFFERENTIATION: Supporting the Range of Learners

Extension Challenge students to use as many different types of blocks as they can.

2B Geoblock Footprints

PAIRS

For complete details about this activity, see Session 1.1, pages 24–27 and consider the following note.

DIFFERENTIATION: Supporting the Range of Learners

Extension Students who are ready for more of a challenge can work on Geoblock Footprints: Set C (M5). They can also try to fill each sheet without using any block more than once.

2C Copying Cube Things

PAIRS

For complete details about this activity, see Session 1.1, pages 24–28 and consider the following note.

DIFFERENTIATION: Supporting the Range of Learners

Extension Adjust the maximum number of cubes (12 to 16) to keep the task manageable but challenging.

ACTIVITY

3 Describing Geoblocks

10 MIN   CLASS

Choose a Geoblock that allows you to introduce a geometric term, such as *face, edge,* or *vertices/corners.* Hold it up and ask students to hold up one that shares a particular characteristic.

Math Note

❶ **Set C's Footprints** Set C has 8 different triangular faces. Some of these are easy to find, but some match only one Geoblock.

Differentiation

❷ **English Language Learners** English Language Learners might need help understanding the related meanings of the words *side, face, footprint,* and *outline* which are used in this session and the next. The words *face* and *footprint* could be especially confusing due to their everyday connotations. You can demonstrate the meanings of these words in context by having students make tracings of their feet and other objects. Diego made an *outline* of his foot, which is one kind of *footprint.* Isabel *outlined* one *face,* or *side,* of this cube; we could also say that she drew a *footprint* of the cube.

▲ Student Activity Book, p. 2

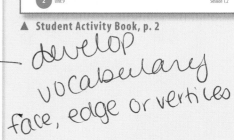
develop vocabulary face, edge or vertices

▲ **Student Activity Book, p. 3**

My block has a side shaped like a [triangle]. Mathematicians call the side of a shape a face. [Trace the [triangular] face.] Find a block in the set near you that has a side, or a face, that is shaped like a triangle.

On the block you chose, point to the face that is shaped like a [triangle].

Students identify attributes of Geoblocks.

Encourage students to take the lead. Ask a volunteer to choose a Geoblock, hold it up for all to see, and name one of its characteristics. Then, have everyone else find a block with the same characteristic.

SESSION FOLLOW-UP
④ Daily Practice and Homework

Daily Practice: For ongoing review, have students complete *Student Activity Book* page 2.

Homework: Students choose an object at home that they think can be recognized from its outline or footprint and trace it on *Student Activity Book* page 3.

Do one or two examples with students as needed, showing them footprints of familiar classroom objects such as your hand, a pair of scissors, or a crayon. Because the class will try to guess what the object is, students should not write the name of their Mystery Object on their drawing.

Student Math Handbook: Students and families may use *Student Math Handbook* pages 83, 85, 86, 90 for reference and review. See pages 124–126 in the back of this unit.

Matching Blocks to Pictures

Math Focus Points

- Developing vocabulary to describe 3-D shapes and their attributes
- Comparing size, shape, and orientation of objects
- Matching a 3-D object to a 2-D picture of the object

Today's Plan		Materials
① DISCUSSION **Mystery Footprints from Home**	10 MIN CLASS	• *Student Activity Book,* p. 3 (from Session 1.2) • Self-stick notes
② ACTIVITY **Block Pictures**	40 MIN CLASS PAIRS	• M9–M12*; T64 • Geoblocks (2 subsets)
③ DISCUSSION **Block Pictures**	10 MIN CLASS	• M10–M12/T65
④ SESSION FOLLOW-UP **Daily Practice and Homework**		• *Student Activity Book,* p. 5 • M13* • Sample Mystery Box (optional)*; extra paper for wrapping • *Student Math Handbook,* pp. 83, 85, 86, 89, 90

*See *Materials to Prepare,* p. 19.

Classroom Routines

Tell a Story Write "1 + 9 = " on chart paper. Ask students to suggest a story problem. After several students have shared ideas, have students solve the problem. If time permits, repeat with "10 − 1 =".

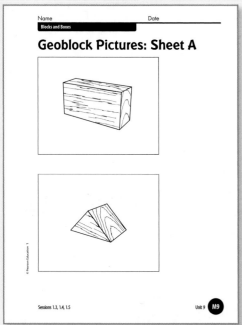

Name _____ Date _____

Blocks and Boxes

Geoblock Pictures: Sheet A

© Pearson Education 1

Sessions 1.3, 1.4, 1.5   Unit 9   **M9**

▲ Resource Masters, M9; T64

DISCUSSION

① Mystery Footprints from Home

10 MIN   **CLASS**

Math Focus Points for Discussion

◆ Matching a 3-D object to a 2-D picture of the object

Begin class by discussing a few of students' Mystery Footprints on *Student Activity Book* page 3.

museum walk and mickey note 03 + lavain sheet it is.

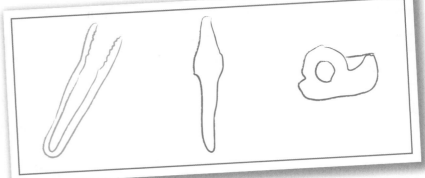

Sample Student Work

What do you think [Allie's] mystery object might be? Why do you think so? Who has a different idea?

After everyone who has an idea has had a chance to guess, ask the student to reveal the identity of the mystery object.

Discuss several mystery footprints. Tell students that you will hang the rest of the mystery footprints in the classroom and explain that they can use self-stick notes or scrap paper to write and post guesses about what they think the objects might be. ①

DIFFERENTIATION: Supporting the Range of Learners

ELL   To encourage English Language Learners to participate in the Mystery Footprints discussions, you can meet with them during Math Workshop to examine some of the footprints together. Some students might not be able to express their guesses in English. If so, encourage them to draw sketches of the objects they think the footprints might represent, locate pictures of the objects in books or magazines, or point out similar objects in the classroom. If necessary, you or a native English-speaking classmate can help English Language Learners write down their guesses. You can use similar strategies to support English Language Learners' participation in the Mystery Box discussions in Sessions 6–8.

② ACTIVITY
Block Pictures

40 MIN   CLASS   PAIRS

Give each pair a copy of Geoblock Pictures: Sheet A (M9).

Challenge students to look in their sets of Geoblocks to find the ones shown in the pictures. Point out that the blocks in the pictures are not the same size as the real blocks. You can relate this to photographs of people; a person in a photograph is smaller than in real life.

After students have had a few minutes to work, display the transparency Geoblock Pictures: Sheet A (T64). Ask students to hold up the block that they think matches the rectangular prism.

It is likely that students will have identified more than one possible block to match each picture. Point out some of the different blocks that match a given picture. Encourage students to talk about how they chose their block and how they could figure out which one is the best match.**❶**

*Was there a block that you thought was right at first, but then you decided that it wasn't? How did you decide which block was the best match?***❷**

After you have discussed the first block on Sheet A, pairs should continue working to find the Geoblocks that match the pictures on Sheets A, B, C, and D (M9–M12).

Students find the Geoblocks that match the pictures on Geoblock Pictures (M9–M12).

Teaching Note

❶ The Best Match Because agreeing on the "correct" block can be challenging, emphasize finding the block that is the best match. Sometimes there are blocks that look quite close to the pictured block, even though they are not the "right" one. The goal is for students to think carefully about alternative blocks and choose blocks that match closely.

Professional Development

❷ Dialogue Box: Comparing Blocks to Pictures, p. 117

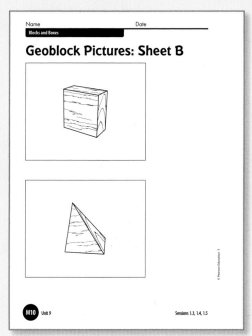

Name _____   Date _____

Blocks and Boxes

Geoblock Pictures: Sheet B

M10 Unit 9   Sessions 1.3, 1.4, 1.5

▲ **Resource Masters, M10**

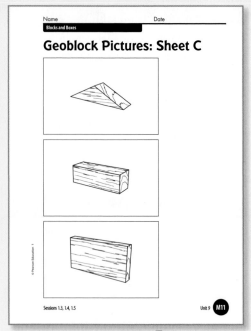

▲ Resource Masters, M11; T65

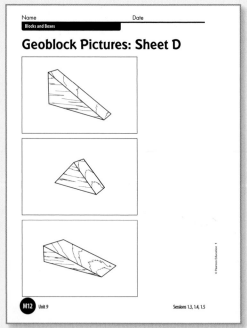

▲ Resource Masters, M12

ONGOING ASSESSMENT: Observing Students at Work

Students look at 2-D photographs of 3-D shapes and find the 3-D blocks that match.

- **How do students approach the task?** Do they seem to know what they are looking for? Do they focus on one face at a time or can they think about more than one? Do they notice which faces are squares, rectangles, and triangles? Which shapes do they find difficult?

- **Do students try to match the Geoblock to the picture carefully, or do they simply select the first Geoblock that has a vague resemblance to the picture?**

- **What language do students use to describe and compare shapes?** Do they talk about attributes of shapes? For example, do they say that shapes are thick, thin, tall, or short? Do they say that one shape is taller or pointier than another?

DIFFERENTIATION: Supporting the Range of Learners

Intervention If you have students who seem overwhelmed by the number and variety of blocks or who have a hard time matching the shapes to the pictures, consider limiting the set of blocks they use. For example, for each sheet, give them 10 or 12 blocks to choose from, including the ones pictured.

Intervention Some students may need more time to freely explore and build with the Geoblocks and more time to find blocks that match given footprints. See Session 1.1, pages 24–25.

Intervention If some students are selecting Geoblocks quickly without carefully comparing blocks, you may try putting out four blocks that match one of the pictures in some way. Include the correct block. Ask students to select the block they think is the best match and to convince you, one by one, why the best match is not one of the other three.

DISCUSSION

③ Block Pictures

10 MIN CLASS

Math Focus Points for Discussion

◆ Matching a 3-D object to a 2-D picture of the object

Spend the last few minutes of this session discussing one or two more Geoblock pictures. Ask students how they went about finding the blocks that might match and how they decided which one was the best match.

Display the transparency of Geoblock Pictures: Sheet C (T65) on the overhead to use in the discussion.

Students discuss how they found the match to the displayed Geoblock picture.

When you were looking for the block that matched this picture, what were you looking for? What's special about this block that helped you find it in the set of Geoblocks?

[Sacha] says that she was looking for a block with a [rectangle]. Everyone take a minute to look in your Geoblock set and find a block that has a [rectangle].

Display the different blocks that students find.

[Sacha] said to look for a block with a [rectangle]. All of these blocks have a [rectangle]. Now what? How can we decide which of these blocks is the best match for this picture?

Encourage students to describe the attributes that each shape has or does not have that help them either eliminate it or decide that it is the best match.

More Mystery Footprints

Write the mystery object for each mystery footprint.

NOTE Students match 2-D outlines to 3-D objects.

1. _____

2. _____

3. _____

Ongoing Review

4. How many more chairs are needed?

People	Chairs
12	10

Ⓐ 12   Ⓒ 3

Ⓑ 10   Ⓓ 2

▲ **Student Activity Book, p. 5**

Continuing w/ vocabulary face, edge, vertices

Teaching Note

❸ Sharing Our Box Collection As students bring in their Mystery Boxes over the next several days, show them how you will organize and store the collection until its unveiling in Session 1.8. Help students wrap any uncovered boxes and number each one. Keep a list of the numbers and corresponding student names, and post it. You may also mark off each number that has been used on a 100 chart.

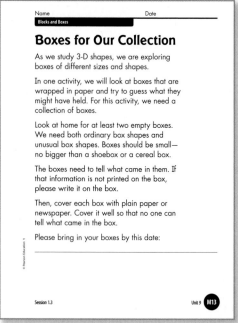

Name _____ Date _____

Blocks and Boxes

Boxes for Our Collection

As we study 3-D shapes, we are exploring boxes of different sizes and shapes.

In one activity, we will look at boxes that are wrapped in paper and try to guess what they might have held. For this activity, we need a collection of boxes.

Look at home for at least two empty boxes. We need both ordinary box shapes and unusual box shapes. Boxes should be small— no bigger than a shoebox or a cereal box.

The boxes need to tell what came in them. If that information is not printed on the box, please write it on the box.

Then, cover each box with plain paper or newspaper. Cover it well so that no one can tell what came in the box.

Please bring in your boxes by this date: _____

Session 1.3   Unit 9 **M13**

▲ **Resource Masters, M13**

SESSION FOLLOW-UP
④ Daily Practice and Homework

 Daily Practice: For reinforcement of this unit's content, have students complete *Student Activity Book* page 5.

Homework: Following the instructions on Boxes for Our Collection (M13), students are to find two empty boxes at home and cover them with heavy paper or newspaper so that no one can tell what was originally inside. Students will be guessing what each box contained, given its size and shape. This activity is similar to Mystery Footprints on *Student Activity Book* page 3.

Point out the date by which you will need the boxes (by Session 1.6), and discuss the size guideline (no bigger than a cereal or shoe box). Showing students a sample Mystery Box may give them a clearer image of what you expect.❸

A student adds a Mystery Box to the class display.

 Student Math Handbook: Students and families may use *Student Math Handbook* pages 83, 85, 86, 89, 90 for reference and review. See pages 124–126 in the back of this unit.

Assessment: Blocks in a Sock

Math Focus Points

◆ Identifying the characteristics of 3-D objects by touch

◆ Matching a 3-D object to a 2-D picture of the object

◆ Matching a 3-D object to a 2-D outline of one of its faces

Today's Plan		Materials
① ACTIVITY **Introducing Blocks in a Sock** `15 MIN` `CLASS`		• M9 • Geoblocks J and P; a sock or small bag
② MATH WORKSHOP **Building and Matching 3-D Shapes** `45 MIN` **②A** Assessment Activity: Blocks in a Sock **②B** Build a Wall **②C** Geoblock Footprints **②D** Copying Cube Things		**②A** • M9–M12*; M14 ☑ * • Geoblocks; socks or small bags **②B** • Materials from Session 1.2, p. 29 **②C** • Materials from Session 1.1, p. 22 • M15–M18* **②D** • Materials from Session 1.1, p. 22
③ SESSION FOLLOW-UP **Daily Practice and Homework**		• *Student Activity Book,* pp. 6–8 • *Student Math Handbook,* pp. 83, 88, 90

*See *Materials to Prepare,* p. 19.

Classroom Routines

Quick Images: Shapes Show transparencies from Shape Cards (T62–T63), beginning with Shape I. Follow the basic *Quick Images* activity. Ask students to describe the shape after it has been drawn. Repeat with Shape K and then Shape N. Compare the three shapes at the end of the activity.

ACTIVITY

Introducing Blocks in a Sock

15 MIN   CLASS

Show students a copy of Geoblock Pictures: Sheet A (M9) and the two Geoblocks (J and P) that are pictured on it.

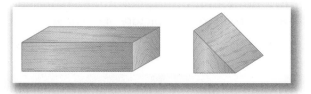

Geoblocks

The other day, we decided that these blocks match the pictures on this sheet. I'm going to put these two blocks in this sock and ask a volunteer to put his or her hand in the sock and try to find this one [hold up Geoblock J, the rectangular prism] just by feeling it.

Give several volunteers a chance to feel inside the sock to try to find Geoblock J. Ask them *not* to pull the block out of the bag. Instead, encourage them to explain how they can tell which block is which.

Students might say:

"I can tell which one it is because it's long and skinny."

"It's shaped like a box."

Finally, ask one or two students to reach in and pull out the block that matches the picture.

Explain that during Math Workshop, students will work in pairs. First, they choose one of the Geoblock Pictures sheets and find the Geoblocks that match. Then, they put the blocks in a sock. Student 1 chooses a picture, and Student 2 tries to pull the matching block out of the sock. Then, they trade roles and do it again.

MATH WORKSHOP

② Building and Matching 3-D Shapes

45 MIN

Students spend most of this session and the next choosing among the following activities. Everyone should work on Blocks in a Sock at some point on both days.

PAIRS

②A Assessment Activity: Blocks in a Sock

For complete details about Blocks in a Sock, see the previous activity in this session and consider the following notes.❶

As students work on Blocks in a Sock today and in Session 1.5, you will have an opportunity to assess the following benchmarks:

- **Benchmark 1:** Attend to features of 3-D shapes, such as overall size and shape, the number and shape of faces, and the number of corners

- **Benchmark 2:** Match a 2-D representation to a 3-D shape or structure

Keep a record on Assessment Checklist: Observing Blocks in a Sock (M14).

Talk with students as they work, asking questions, such as these:

- Why do you think that block is the block in the picture? What did you notice about the block in the picture that helped you find the actual Geoblock?

- You are trying to find this block in your sock. Can you tell me what you are feeling for? What will help you know that you are touching the right block?

You can also choose a block that does *not* match but is close in some way and ask this question:

Why do you think this isn't the block in the picture?

Teaching Note

❶ **Organizing Blocks in a Sock** At each table with three pairs, put Geoblock Pictures A–D (M9–M12) and a subset of Geoblocks. Each pair of students chooses a sheet to begin. Because each pair is using a different sheet, students will not need the same blocks at the same time. When they have finished, they should trade sheets.

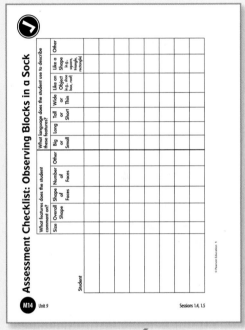

▲ **Resource Masters, M14**

Name _____ Date _____

Blocks and Boxes

Geoblock Footprints: Set D

Sessions 1.4, 1.5   Unit 9 **M15**

▲ **Resource Masters, M15–M16**

Name _____ Date _____

Blocks and Boxes

Geoblock Footprints: Set F

Sessions 1.4, 1.5   Unit 9 **M17**

▲ **Resource Masters, M17–M18**

ONGOING ASSESSMENT: Observing Students at Work

Students identify a 3-D object on the basis of a 2-D photograph and touch.

- **How do students find the correct 3-D blocks to put in the sock based on the 2-D photographs?**

- **How do students use touch and the matching 2-D picture to identify a 3-D block?** Do students examine the pictures of both blocks to help them?

- **What characteristics of the blocks do students use to do both of the previous tasks?** The shapes of the faces? The size (e.g., dimensions) of the blocks? Do they use only one characteristic or are they able to consider more?

DIFFERENTIATION: Supporting the Range of Learners

Intervention Some students are more comfortable with the sheets that show only two Geoblocks (Sheets A and B), whereas others may want to try a sheet with three (Sheets C and D).

Students play Blocks in a Sock.

Extension Students ready for more of a challenge can combine a 2-block sheet with a 3-block sheet and hide five blocks in the sock.

2B Build a Wall

PAIRS

For complete details about this activity, see Session 1.2, pages 30–31, and consider the following note.

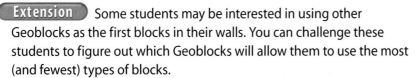

DIFFERENTIATION: Supporting the Range of Learners

Extension Some students may be interested in using other Geoblocks as the first blocks in their walls. You can challenge these students to figure out which Geoblocks will allow them to use the most (and fewest) types of blocks.

2C Geoblock Footprints

PAIRS

Students who have not yet completed Geoblock Footprints: Sets A, B, and C (M1; M2; M5) should do so now. Others can find matches for the footprints on Sets D through G (M15–M18). Each of these sheets shows three to six copies of the same footprint. Students are to find a different block for each footprint on the sheet.

For complete details about this activity, see Session 1.1, pages 24–27.

2D Copying Cube Things

PAIRS

For complete details about this activity, see Session 1.1, pages 24–28.

---

3 SESSION FOLLOW-UP
Daily Practice and Homework

 Daily Practice: For ongoing review, have students complete *Student Activity Book* page 6.

 Homework: Students circle the object that has the same shape as the pictured Geoblocks on *Student Activity Book* pages 7–8. ❷

 Student Math Handbook: Students and families may use *Student Math Handbook* pages 83, 88, 90 for reference and review. See pages 124–126 in the back of this unit.

Teaching Note

❷ **Mystery Box Reminder** Remind students to bring in their Mystery Boxes by Session 1.6.

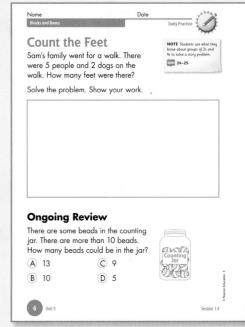

Name _____ Date _____
Blocks and Boxes   Daily Practice

Count the Feet
Sam's family went for a walk. There were 5 people and 2 dogs on the walk. How many feet were there?

NOTE Students use what they know about groups of 2s and 4s to solve a story problem.
Skill 24–25

Solve the problem. Show your work.

Ongoing Review
There are some beads in the counting jar. There are more than 10 beads. How many beads could be in the jar?

(A) 13   (C) 9
(B) 10   (D) 5

6 Unit 9   Session 1.4

▲ Student Activity Book, p. 6

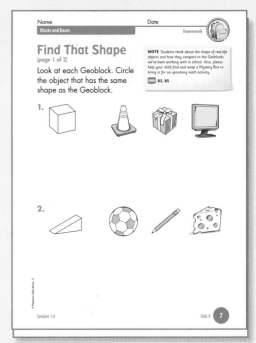

Name _____ Date _____
Blocks and Boxes   Homework

Find That Shape
(page 1 of 2)
Look at each Geoblock. Circle the object that has the same shape as the Geoblock.

NOTE Students think about the shape of real-life objects and how they compare to the Geoblocks we've been working with in school. Also, please help your child find and wrap a Mystery Box to bring in for an upcoming math activity.
Skill 83, 85

1.

2.

Session 1.4   Unit 9 7

▲ Student Activity Book, pp. 7–8

Assessment: Matching Blocks to Outlines

Math Focus Points

◆ Identifying the characteristics of 3-D objects by touch

◆ Matching a 3-D object to a 2-D picture o f the object

◆ Matching a 3-D object to a 2-D outline of one of its faces

Today's Plan		Materials
1 ASSESSMENT ACTIVITY **Matching Blocks to Outlines**	✓ 🕐 15 MIN 👥 CLASS 🧍 INDIVIDUALS	• M19* • Geoblocks S, V, C, O, U, X, J, G (as needed for Intervention)
2 MATH WORKSHOP **Building and Matching 3-D Shapes** **2A** Assessment Activity: Blocks in a Sock **2B** Build a Wall **2C** Geoblock Footprints **2D** Copying Cube Things	🕐 30 MIN	**2A** • Materials from Session 1.4, p. 39 **2B** • Materials from Session 1.2, p. 29 **2C** • Materials from Session 1.1, p. 22 **2D** • Materials from Session 1.1, p. 22
3 DISCUSSION **Blocks in a Sock**	🕐 15 MIN 👥 CLASS	• Geoblocks R, O, S, M, P, C, Q, N, and T • T66
4 SESSION FOLLOW-UP **Daily Practice and Homework**		• *Student Activity Book,* pp. 9–10 • *Student Math Handbook,* pp. 83, 88, 90

*See *Materials to Prepare,* p. 21.

Classroom Routines

Quick Survey: Triangle or Rectangle? On chart paper, create a vertical 2-column table, titled "Is it easier to draw a triangle or a rectangle?" with a picture of a triangle and a picture of a rectangle as column headings. Use Ts and Rs to record students' responses and then count them. After counting the responses, briefly discuss the results of the survey.

ASSESSMENT ACTIVITY
Matching Blocks to Outlines

15 MIN   CLASS   INDIVIDUALS

This assessment activity addresses Benchmark 2: Match a 2-D representation to a 3-D shape or structure.

Explain that students will begin work today by completing Assessment: Matching Blocks to Outlines (M19) and that they will work individually so that you can see how far they have come in their thinking about shapes.

Show students the sheet and explain the task. Compare the task to the Geoblock Footprints activity that they have been doing in Math Workshop.

ONGOING ASSESSMENT: Observing Students at Work

Students look at pictures of Geoblocks and at the shapes of Geoblock faces. They match each block to its outline.❶

- **Do students correctly match the blocks to footprints?** What reasoning do they give? What language do they use to describe and compare the shapes and footprints?

DIFFERENTIATION: Supporting the Range of Learners

(Intervention) Some students may benefit from working with actual Geoblocks. Using the collection of Geoblocks you have gathered for this assessment (S, V, C, O, U, X, J, G), ask these students to find the blocks pictured in the top row of the sheet. Then, ask them to show you which block matches which footprint.

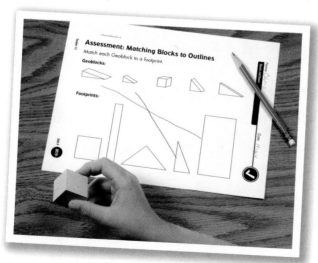

A student uses Geoblocks to help him with the assessment.

Professional Development

❶ **Teacher Note:** Assessment: Matching Blocks to Outlines, p. 109

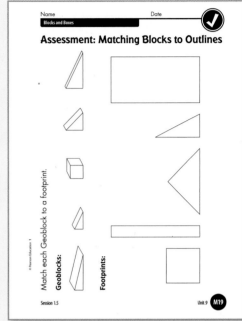

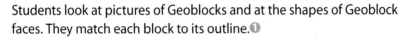

▲ **Resource Masters, M19** *PORTFOLIO*

MATH WORKSHOP

② Building and Matching 3-D Shapes

30 MIN

As students finish the assessment, they can choose from the following activities. Everyone should work on *Blocks in a Sock* at some point today.

②A Assessment Activity: Blocks in a Sock

PAIRS

For complete details about this activity, see Session 1.4, pages 40–41.

Continue to use Assessment Checklist: Observing: Blocks in a Sock (M14) to record your observations.

②B Build a Wall

 PAIRS

For complete details about this activity, see Sessions 1.2, pages 30–31, and 1.4, pages 42–43.

②C Geoblock Footprints

 PAIRS

For complete details about this activity, see Sessions 1.1, pages 24–27, and 1.4, page 43.

②D Copying Cube Things

 PAIRS

For complete details about this activity, see Session 1.1, pages 24–28.

DISCUSSION

③ Blocks in a Sock

15 MIN   CLASS

Math Focus Points for Discussion

◆ Identifying the characteristics of 3-D objects by touch

◆ Matching a 3-D object to a 2-D picture of the object

Spend a few minutes discussing the blocks on Geoblock Pictures: Sheet D (T66). Display the collection of Geoblocks that you have gathered for this discussion: Geoblocks R, O, S, M, P, C, Q, N, and T.

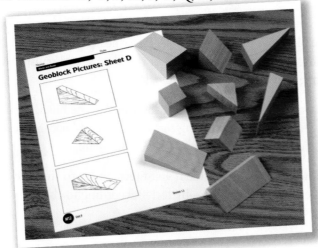

Students match Geoblocks (3-D) and pictures (2-D).

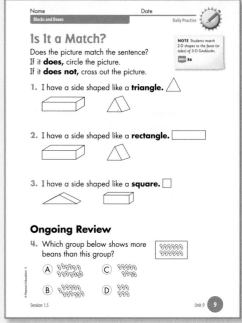

▲ **Student Activity Book, p. 9**

Gather students around. Ask them to study the pictures on the sheet and the Geoblocks in the set and to find a Geoblock that matches each illustration. After a few minutes, ask a volunteer to choose one of the pictures, hold up the Geoblock that he or she thinks is the best match, and explain why. Ask questions that encourage students to describe the important characteristics of the Geoblock in question.

[Deshawn] said that he picked this block [Geoblock S] to match the bottom picture because it looks like a ramp. [Deshawn], I was thinking that this top picture looks a little like a ramp, too. How did you know that your block matches the bottom picture and not the top one?

[Deshawn] says that his block looks like a ramp *and* it's wide and flat [trace the large rectangular face of Geoblock S]. Does anyone think that another block is the best match for this picture?

Ask other volunteers to describe how they chose the best match for the other pictures. Then, place the three matching Geoblocks in a sock or bag. Ask a volunteer to choose a picture on the sheet. Explain that you will try to find the Geoblock that matches the picture without looking but by feeling the Geoblocks in the sock. Ask students to give you advice based on the set of pictures.

Teaching Notes

❷ Mystery Objects in Class You can also encourage conversations about shape, size, and texture by doing this activity in school with common classroom objects.

❸ Mystery Box Reminder Remind students to bring in their Mystery Boxes for the next session. (See Session Follow-Up in Session 1.3.)

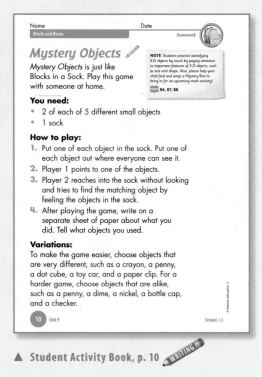

▲ **Student Activity Book, p. 10**

What should I be thinking about as I feel the blocks? If I am looking for the block in this picture [point to a picture on the sheet], is there something special I should be feeling for?

Again, encourage students to describe the important characteristics of the blocks as they offer advice. After hearing students' suggestions and choosing a block, pull out all of the blocks, and revisit students' advice while they can see all three blocks.

[Talisa] said that I should be looking for the block that probably fits in my hand without sticking out [place each block in your hand and try to close your fist around it]. Was that helpful advice?

If there is time, ask student volunteers to try to find the blocks in the other two illustrations—by feel—according to the advice of their classmates.

SESSION FOLLOW-UP

4 Daily Practice and Homework

Daily Practice: For reinforcement of this unit's content, have students complete *Student Activity Book* page 9.

Homework: Students play a game similar to the activity, Blocks in a Sock, with someone outside school and write about their experience on *Student Activity Book* page 10.❷ Students who are not comfortable writing may give their responses orally and ask a family member to write for them.❸

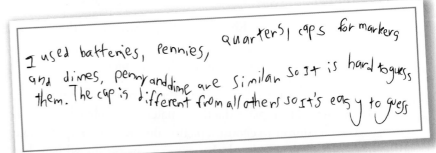

Sample Student Work

Student Math Handbook: Students and families may use *Student Math Handbook* pages 83, 88, 90 for reference and review. See pages 124–126 in the back of this unit.

What Kind of Box Is It?

Math Focus Points

◆ Relating the size and shape of an object to its use

◆ Describing a rectangular prism

◆ Making 3-D objects out of 2-D pieces

Today's Plan		Materials
ACTIVITY ① Looking at Mystery Boxes	10 MIN CLASS	• Mystery Box Collection*; blank pieces of paper or large index cards (optional); clear or masking tape (optional)
ACTIVITY ② How Many Faces?	10 MIN PAIRS CLASS	• Mystery Box Collection (from Activity 1)
ACTIVITY ③ Making Boxes with Cards	40 MIN CLASS PAIRS	• Box Pieces: Set A*; demonstration box*; clear or masking tape; scissors; connecting cubes; collection of small objects* • Envelopes (1 per pair)
SESSION FOLLOW-UP ④ Daily Practice		• *Student Activity Book,* p. 11 • *Student Math Handbook,* pp. 86, 87

*See *Materials to Prepare,* p. 21.

Classroom Routines

Tell a Story Write "9 + 9 =" on chart paper. Ask students to suggest a story problem. After several students have shared ideas, have students solve the problem. If time permits, repeat with "10 + 8 =".

ACTIVITY

 Looking at Mystery Boxes

10 MIN   CLASS

From the Mystery Box collection, choose several boxes that are quite different from one another in size and shape and place them on a separate table. Include a few that you think will be distinctive and recognizable and one or two that you think will be less familiar. For example, you may choose a toothpaste box, a small jewelry box, an oatmeal box (a cylinder), a shoebox, and a cereal box.

Hold up one box and ask students to visualize what it might have contained.

Take a minute and look carefully at Mystery Box [4]. Don't say anything yet. Look at the size and shape and think about what kind of box you think it is. What do you think it had inside?

Tape a piece of paper or large index card to the box and write students' suggestions on it or record their guesses right on the box. Ask follow-up questions that focus students' attention on the size and shape of the box, such as the following:

- [Libby] guessed that this box might have held [earrings], and [Seth] said a [bracelet]. Why do you think these might be good guesses?

- [Neil] thinks Mystery Box [5] might be a [raisin] box and [Jacinta] thinks that it's [gum] that comes in a box. Why do you think Box [5] might not be a [raisin or gum box]?

- No one thought that Mystery Box [13] was a shoebox. Why not?

Discuss a few suggestions, and then repeat this process with several other boxes. In addition to asking questions about each box, encourage students to compare boxes.

Suppose that I said that one of these boxes is a cereal box. Which one would you think it is? Why do you think it's that one rather than this one?

Explain that, over the course of the next few days, students will make guesses about each box. Show students where the boxes will be located. Explain how they will record their guesses when they can work on the activity (e.g., during Math Workshop, first thing in the morning, and so on). Let them know that in a few days, the Mystery Boxes will be unwrapped to see what they really are.

ACTIVITY

② How Many Faces?

10 MIN   PAIRS   CLASS

Give each pair a box from the Mystery Box collection.

If I were to ask how many flat sides your box has, what would you think I meant? What does "a flat side" mean?

After taking students' suggestions, indicate a face on several different boxes.

Many people call these sides. *Mathematicians call them* faces.❶ *Take a minute to look at your box. Work with your partner to figure out how many faces (or sides) it has.*❷ *Don't tell me yet. I want you to be able to explain how you are sure.*

Give students a minute or two to study their boxes before asking how many faces their boxes have and how they know for sure. Encourage them to say more than "I counted" and to think about the way the faces are arranged in relation to one another.

Pairs determine the number of sides on their Mystery Boxes.

How can you be sure that you counted each face? How do you know that you didn't skip one or count one twice? Who had a way of keeping track?

Most boxes will be rectangular prisms with three pairs of opposite faces (six faces in all). If you have any cylindrical or other-shaped Mystery Boxes, encourage students to discuss how the curved side should be counted.❸

Math Note

❶ **Vocabulary** Continue to model the use of mathematical vocabulary (e.g., faces) with students, but expect that they may use a variety of informal terms (e.g., sides).

Professional Development

❷ **Teacher Note:** Types of 3-D Shapes, p. 107

Teaching Notes

❸ **What About Cylinders?** Students can find more information about shapes with curved sides in the *Student Math Handbook*.

Teaching Notes

④ Displaying the Mystery Boxes Ask student helpers to collect all the Mystery Boxes and place them in the display area.

⑤ Books About Boxes You can use children's literature to introduce this activity. *The House,* by Monique Felix, gives a wonderful visual account of putting together a house (e.g., box) by cutting and folding paper. You could also use books about children who imagine many different uses for a box, such as *A Box Can Be Many Things* by Dana Meachen Rau and *Christina Katerina and the Box* by Patricia Lee Gauch.

End this discussion by summarizing the results and asking students to think about what different groups of boxes have in common.

It seems that most of our boxes have six faces. Hold up your box if you think it has six faces. Take a look. What's the same about all these boxes? Who has a box that doesn't have six faces? How many faces does it have?

Although students are unlikely to generate a complete description of a rectangular prism, they should be beginning to notice many of the features of this common 3-D shape.④

ACTIVITY

③ Making Boxes with Cards

40 MIN   CLASS   PAIRS

Prepare one set of Box Pieces: Set A per pair. Set A has 12 box pieces in five sizes. For each set use seven 3″ x 5″ cards and four 5″ x 8″ cards. Cut the cards as shown below, and put each set in an envelope labeled, "Box Pieces: Set A."

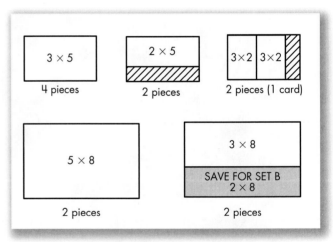

For the rest of this session and most of the next, students will be constructing 3-D boxes from 2-D pieces.⑤

Show students the box you have made and an envelope of Box Pieces: Set A. Relate the box pieces to the faces students just counted on their Mystery Boxes.

You are going to be making your own box, like this one [hold up demonstration box]. You and your partner will get a set of flat pieces in all different sizes, like these [hold up envelope and take out remaining box pieces]. But they won't all fit together. It's like a puzzle. Your job is to figure out which flat pieces to put together and how to tape them together to make a box that has sides, a bottom, and a top.❻

Ask a volunteer to suggest two pieces that could be taped together to start a box. Demonstrate how to tape these pieces together and explain any guidelines you have about the use of tape.❼ If you think it necessary, show how to attach one more piece to the box.

When students understand the task, give each pair an envelope of Box Pieces: Set A and challenge them to use the pieces to make two different boxes.❽

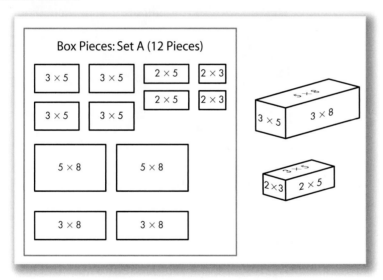

The pieces in Set A will make two different boxes.

Professional Development

❻ **Teacher Note:** Students Make Their Own Boxes, p. 111

Teaching Notes

❼ **Planning Ahead** Encourage students to plan before they tape, perhaps by holding pieces next to each other to see whether they fit and how they want to put them together. Let students know that, if they do tape some pieces in error, they can just cut through the tape to take them apart.

❽ **Save the Boxes** At the end of the session, ask all students to initial the box that they are working on—along with any that they have completed—and place them in a designated area. Explain that they will have more time to complete their boxes and build additional ones tomorrow.

ONGOING ASSESSMENT: Observing Students at Work

Students explore the characteristics of rectangular prisms—how faces come together at edges and how opposite sides of a prism are the same size and shape—and the ways in which 2-D shapes can be put together to make a 3-D shape.

- **How do students begin?** Do they lay out the pieces on the table and see how they can "fold" them up into a box? Do they choose adjacent faces with edges of equal lengths? Do they find cards of the same size and shape to use as opposite faces?

- **What do students do when they run into a problem?** Do they try a different piece or combination of pieces? Do they start making better choices as they learn what does not work? Can they figure out a way to finish their box, even if the result is not a conventional box?

Students work together to make a box from Box Pieces: Set A.

DIFFERENTIATION: Supporting the Range of Learners

This is a challenging activity for many first graders because it involves visualizing how 2-D shapes can go together to make a 3-D shape and because it requires a fair amount of fine motor coordination.⑨

Intervention Some students may benefit from using one of the Mystery Boxes as a model.

Intervention Students who have trouble manipulating the cards and taping them together may benefit from a variation of the activity. Give these students a small object from the collection that you prepared ahead of time. Ask them to use connecting cubes to make a box that is just the right size to hold it. Note whether students use the size of the object to inform their work and whether they are able to construct a box with opposite faces that are the same size and shape.

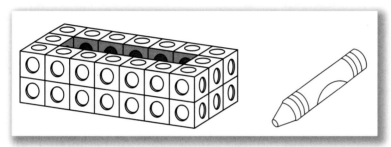

Extension Students who are able to construct two different boxes from Box Pieces: Set A in the time allotted can also work on this task.

SESSION FOLLOW-UP

④ Daily Practice

 Daily Practice: For ongoing review, have students complete *Student Activity Book* page 11.

 Student Math Handbook: Students and families may use *Student Math Handbook* pages 86, 87 for reference and review. See pages 124–126 in the back of this unit.

Teaching Note

⑨ **Expect a Wide Range of Boxes** Some students will make a standard box shape with opposite faces the same size. Others will cut or bend pieces to make them fit together. Remember that the benefit of this activity is in the experience—students must pay close attention to features of 3-D shapes as they attempt to construct a rectangular prism from 2-D pieces—and that students will revisit these ideas in Grade 2.

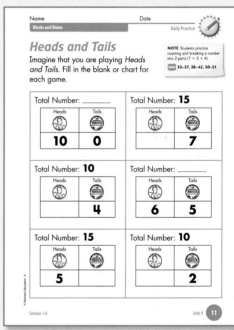

▲ Student Activity Book, p. 11

Making Boxes

Math Focus Points

◆ Making 3-D objects out of 2-D pieces

◆ Comparing rectangular prisms

Today's Plan			Materials
ACTIVITY ① **Making Boxes with Cards**	🕐 40 MIN	👥 PAIRS	• Materials from Session 1.6, p. 52 • Box Pieces: Set B*
DISCUSSION ② **Comparing Boxes**	🕐 20 MIN	👥👥 CLASS 👥 PAIRS	• Students' boxes
SESSION FOLLOW-UP ③ **Daily Practice**			• *Student Activity Book,* p. 12 • *Student Math Handbook,* pp. 85, 86, 87

*See *Materials to Prepare,* p. 21.

Classroom Routines

Morning Meeting: Time Follow your daily *Morning Meeting* Routine. During *Daily Schedule,* post the time of events on the classroom schedule in both analog and digital representations. Focusing on activities that start on the hour, ask students questions about what time different activities happen.

What's happening at 9 o'clock this morning? **(science)** What time does [math] start? **(10:00)** What time is dismissal? **(2:00)**

ACTIVITY

① Making Boxes with Cards

40 MIN PAIRS

For complete details about this activity, see Session 1.6, pages 52–54 and consider the following notes.❶

DIFFERENTIATION: Supporting the Range of Learners

Extension Students who make both boxes from Box Pieces: Set A can try making boxes from Box Pieces: Set B. Six new boxes can be made from Set B. Challenge students to make ones that are a different size and shape from the boxes they have made already.

To prepare Box Pieces: Set B, use eighteen 3″ x 5″ cards and eight 5″ x 8″ cards. Cut the cards as shown below, producing 44 box pieces in seven sizes. Also add the extra 2″ x 8″ pieces you saved from cutting up Box Pieces: Set A from Session 1.6. This will be enough pieces for 5 or 6 pairs to make one box each. Double the quantity for 10 or 11 pairs, and triple it for 15 or 16. Sort the box pieces by size onto seven paper plates or box lids. The pieces in Set B allow six new possible boxes.

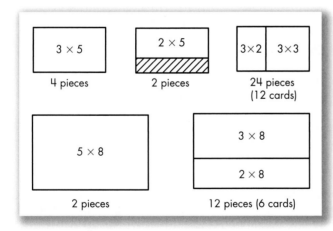

Teaching Note

❶ **Remember the Mystery Boxes** Keep the class collection of Mystery Boxes on display and remind students to keep writing their guesses about what the boxes held.

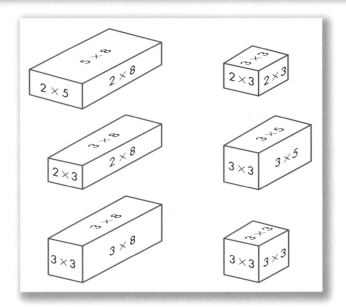

Math Note

❷ **Same Shape, Different Orientation** Some students may not see boxes that are the same size and shape but turned differently as the same. For example, when the 3″ x 5″ x 8″ box stands with the 3″ x 5″ card on the bottom, it looks tall and not very wide. With the 5″ x 8″ card on the bottom, the same box looks long and wide but not very tall. Engage students in conversations about why they think boxes are or are not the same. You may put out three or four boxes and then show another box that is the same size and shape as one of them but in a different position. Ask which box it matches.

DISCUSSION

❷ Comparing Boxes

20 MIN   CLASS   PAIRS

Math Focus Points for Discussion

◆ Comparing rectangular prisms

Gather students together to discuss the boxes that they made today and in Session 1.6. Ask pairs to sit together with their boxes.

Begin by taking a box from one pair of students. Ask everyone who has made the same box to hold it up. When the class agrees that everyone is holding up the same box, have pairs put that box aside.❷

Now hold up another box from a different pair of students. Again, ask students who made the same box to hold it up and then put it aside. Repeat until all the different boxes have been shown.

Students share and compare the boxes that they made.

Collect one example of each different box and start a display. Students can compare these boxes with the new ones that they make. As students go back to their box work in Session 1.8, you can challenge them to construct boxes that are different from those in the display.

SESSION FOLLOW-UP

③ Daily Practice

 **Daily Practice:** For reinforcement of this unit's content, have students complete *Student Activity Book* page 12.

Student Math Handbook: Students and families may use *Student Math Handbook* pages 85, 86, 87 for reference and review. See pages 124–126 in the back of this unit.

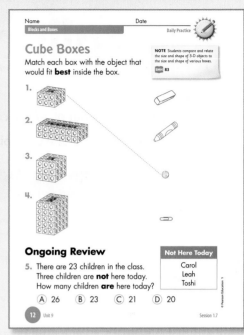

▲ **Student Activity Book, p. 12**

Revealing the Mystery Boxes

Math Focus Points

◆ Making 3-D objects out of 2-D pieces

◆ Relating the size and shape of an object to its use

Today's Plan		Materials
① ACTIVITY **Making Boxes with Cards**	40 MIN PAIRS	• Materials from Session 1.6, p. 49 and 1.7, p. 56 • Index cards
② DISCUSSION **Revealing the Mystery Boxes**	20 MIN CLASS	• Collection of Mystery Boxes (from Session 1.6)
③ SESSION FOLLOW-UP **Daily Practice**		• *Student Activity Book,* p. 13 • *Student Math Handbook,* pp. 85, 86, 87

Classroom Routines

Quick Survey: Morning, Afternoon, or Night? On chart paper, create a vertical 3-column table, titled "Which do you like best: morning, afternoon, or night?" with the words "Morning," "Afternoon," and "Night" as column headings. Use tally marks to record students' responses, and then count them by 5s and 1s. After counting the responses, briefly discuss the results of the survey.

ACTIVITY

1 Making Boxes with Cards

40 MIN   PAIRS

For complete details about this activity, see Sessions 1.6 and 1.7, pages 52–55 and page 57–58 and consider the following note.**❶**

DIFFERENTIATION: Supporting the Range of Learners

Extension Students who want more of a challenge can try to cut their own pieces—instead of starting with a prepared set—to make boxes in shapes and sizes of their own choosing.

DISCUSSION

2 Revealing the Mystery Boxes

20 MIN   CLASS

Math Focus Points for Discussion

◆ Relating the size and shape of an object to its use

Gather students where they can see the Mystery Boxes and ask them to agree on one box that they are sure they can identify. Encourage students to share their ideas about what it held and to describe what they noticed about its size and shape that gave them clues.**❷**

Then, unwrap and reveal the box. Repeat this with two or three other boxes—always choosing ones that students seem to have a definite idea about. Then, ask whether there are any boxes that students are particularly curious about.**❸**

The teacher reveals a Mystery Box to the class.

Name _____ Date _____
Blocks and Boxes   Daily Practice

Missing Numbers 1
Write the missing numbers on the
counting strips.

NOTE Students practice counting,
writing, and sequencing numbers.
SMH 21–23, 31

8	16	37	54
9	17	38	55
10	18	39	56

Session 1.8   Unit 9 13

▲ **Student Activity Book, p. 13**

Are there any boxes that are really a mystery to you? Is there one that you want me to unwrap because it was so hard to guess?

Allow several students to choose a box to unwrap.

SESSION FOLLOW-UP

 3 Daily Practice

 Daily Practice: For ongoing review, have students complete *Student Activity Book* page 13.

Student Math Handbook: Students and families may use *Student Math Handbook* pages 85, 86, 87 for reference and review. See pages 124–126 in the back of this unit.

Mathematical Emphases

Features of Shape Describing and comparing 2-D and 3-D shapes

Math Focus Points

◆ Observing and describing characteristics of 3-D shapes

◆ Recognizing shapes in the world

◆ Describing 3-D structures

Features of Shape Exploring the relationships between 2-D and 3-D shapes

Math Focus Points

◆ Making a 2-D representation of a 3-D object or structure

◆ Building a 3-D construction from a 2-D representation

This Investigation also focuses on

◆ Planning a geometric structure with limited space and materials

◆ Visualizing and estimating the paces and turns required to follow a particular path

◆ Giving, following, and recording directions for following a path

◆ Counting and adding to compare the distances of different paths

Building a Block Town

	Student Activity Book	Student Math Handbook	Professional Development: Read Ahead of Time	
SESSION 2.1 p. 68				
Drawing Geoblocks Students draw a picture of a given Geoblock building as accurately as they can. Class discussion focuses on strategies for making a 2-D picture of a 3-D object. Then, each student builds and draws a picture of a Geoblock building.	14–15	84	• **Teacher Note:** Students Draw in 3-D, p. 113 • **Dialogue Box:** Making It Look 3-D, p. 121	
SESSION 2.2 p. 74				
Building from a Plan Each student constructs a Geoblock building and then tries to represent the geometric characteristics of it on paper. Then, pairs of students trade pictures and use them as plans to construct a building.	17	84, 91		
SESSION 2.3 p. 79				
Buildings for Our Town Students discuss buildings they have seen in their community and buildings they want their class Geoblock town to have. Pairs choose a building to design, build, and draw for the class town.	15, 18	83, 84, 91	• **Dialogue Box:** Arcades, Parks, and Hardware Stores, p. 123	
SESSION 2.4 p. 84				
Building Our Town Pairs finish drawing plans of their buildings. They use these 2-D plans to construct 3-D buildings on the large street grid and write a few sentences about their buildings. Class discussion focuses on a name for the town.	19	85, 91		

Classroom Routines See page 14 for an overview.

Morning Meeting

- **Yearly weather data chart**

Quick Images

- **T61–T63, Shape Cards [Overhead Transparency icon] from Investigation 1**

Quick Survey

- ***Quick Survey*** **charts for Sessions 2.3 and 2.6. See pages 79 and 92.**

Tell a Story

- **Chart paper**

Materials to Gather	Materials to Prepare
• **Chart paper** • **Geoblocks** (4 subsets) • For Children's Literature suggestions, see page 71 (optional).	• **M20, Ways to Draw Blocks** Make copies. Use a copier to enlarge one copy to post. • **Geoblock buildings** Make enough simple Geoblock buildings so that each student can see one clearly. Use 3–4 different Geoblocks per building. The buildings need not be identical. (1 per 4 students) For sample buildings, see Session 2.1, p. 69. • **Shapes with curved sides** If your classroom doesn't have any, borrow some building blocks that have curved sides, such as cylinders, cones, and arches, and use them for the activities that require Geoblocks. (optional; as needed)
• **Materials for Building and Drawing** See Session 2.1.	• **M21–22, Family Letter** Make copies. (1 per student)
• **Chart paper** • **Geoblocks** (4 subsets) • **5″ x 8″ index cards or half-sheets of 8 $\frac{1}{2}$″ x 11″ paper** (1 per pair) • **Markers or crayons** (as needed) • **Children's books about unusual buildings or houses** (optional) • **Shapes with curved sides** (optional; from Session 2.1)	• **Large Street Grid** Make a large street grid for the class town on poster board or large paper using Street Grid (M23) as a model. If students use 5″ x 8″ index cards, make a 30″ x 48″ grid from a 6-by-6 array of 5″ x 8″ rectangles. If students build on half-sheets of letter-size paper, make your grid 33″ x 51″. Find a location such as on a table or on the floor where you can leave the grid for several days as students work on the town.
• **Materials for Designing Buildings for Our Town** See Session 2.3. • **Students' plans** (from Sessions 2.3 and Session 2.4)	• **M24, Describing My Building** Make copies. (1 per pair)

[Overhead Transparency icon] Overhead Transparency

Building a Block Town,
continued

	Student Activity Book	Student Math Handbook	Professional Development: Read Ahead of Time	
SESSION 2.5 p. 89				
Building Our Town, *continued* Individuals finish writing about their building, and pairs finish erecting their buildings on the class grid. The class chooses a name for the town.	20–21	85, 91		
SESSION 2.6 p. 92				
Giving Directions Students give directions from one place to another in the classroom and on a map of the class town. The class develops a code for giving directions, and students use this code to record trips through the class town.	23	92		
SESSION 2.7 p. 99				
Giving Directions, *continued* Students give directions that get a robot to its destination quickly and slowly and compare the two paths. Then they continue to use the class code to record trips through the class town.	24–29	92		
SESSION 2.8 p. 103				
End-of-Unit Assessment Students are given 2-D representations of four different buildings. They look at four Geoblock buildings and decide which plan represents which building.	31	85, 86, 90, 91	• **Teacher Note:** End-of-Unit Assessment: Matching Plans to Buildings, p. 115	

Materials to Gather	Materials to Prepare
• **M23, Street Grid** (1 copy; from Session 2.3) • **M24, Describing My Building** (1 per student; from Session 2.4) • **Materials for Building Our Buildings** See Session 2.4. • **Students' plans** (from Sessions 2.3 and 2.4) • **Class town**	
• **Toy person or car, small block or counter, or small cardboard pointer** (1 per pair) • **Lined paper** (1 per pair) • **Chart paper**	• **M23, Street Grid** Use this sheet to create the map of the class town. • **Map of the class town** When the town is complete, write the names of all its buildings (in the right locations) on a copy of Street Grid (M23). Add some simple drawings to help nonreaders identify each location. Indicate the location of the entrance to each building on the grid by putting a large dot in the appropriate corner of its rectangle. For a sample map, see Session 2.6, page 95. Make copies. (1 per pair) • **T67, Street Grid** 🖳 Fill in the buildings of the class town.
• **Toy person or car, small block or counter, or small cardboard pointer** (as needed) • **Materials for Paths Through Town** See Session 2.6.	
• **M25, Four Buildings** • **Blank paper** • **Geoblocks** (4 subsets)	• **M26, End-of-Unit Assessment: Matching Plans to Buildings** Make copies. (1 per student) • **Four Geoblock buildings with letter labels** Use the drawings on Four Buildings (M25) to set up and label Buildings A, B, C, and D. Depending on the number of students and available space in your classroom, assemble several sets of the four Geoblock buildings. See the photo in Session 2.8, p. 104.

🖳 Overhead Transparency

Drawing Geoblocks

Math Focus Points

◆ Observing and describing characteristics of 3-D shapes

◆ Making a 2-D representation of a 3-D object or structure

Vocabulary

three-dimensional (3-D)
two-dimensional (2-D)

Today's Plan		Materials
ACTIVITY **① Introducing Drawing Geoblock Buildings**	20 MIN CLASS INDIVIDUALS	• Geoblock buildings*
DISCUSSION **② Drawing Geoblock Buildings**	10 MIN CLASS	• Drawings of Geoblock buildings (from Activity 1); chart paper • For Children's Literature suggestions, see page 71 (optional).
ACTIVITY **③ Building and Drawing**	30 MIN INDIVIDUALS	• M20* • Chart: "Drawing Geoblocks" (from Activity 2); Geoblocks*
SESSION FOLLOW-UP **④ Daily Practice and Homework**		• *Student Activity Book,* pp. 14–15 • *Student Math Handbook,* p. 84

*See *Materials to Prepare,* p. 65.

Classroom Routines

Tell a Story Write "10 + 5 =" on chart paper. Ask students to suggest a story problem. After several students have shared ideas, have students solve the problem. If time permits, repeat using "15 − 5 =".

ACTIVITY

Introducing Drawing Geoblock Buildings

20 MIN   CLASS   INDIVIDUALS

Set up enough small Geoblock buildings so that each student can see one clearly.

Sample Geoblock buildings

Explain that students are to draw the building that is closest to them.

Today we're going to try to draw blocks so that they look three-dimensional. What does that mean when I say a drawing can look three-dimensional (or 3-D)?

Help students understand the difference between two-dimensional (or 2-D) and 3-D and how a 2-D picture that is flat on a piece of paper can look 3-D. ❶

Talk about trying to make pictures look three-dimensional, but keep it brief because students will discuss strategies for making 2-D representations of 3-D objects after they have had time to experiment with drawing a building. Reassure students that this kind of drawing is rather difficult and that you are all going to be experimenting to see how to make a picture of a block building not look flat.

It takes years for adults to learn how to do really good drawings of 3-D shapes. Your job is to do the best you can. Your drawing won't look exactly the same as the building, but try to draw it in a way that helps us see which blocks I used. Then we'll look at some of your pictures and see whether they give us some ideas about how to make shapes look 3-D on paper. ❷

Teaching Note

❶ **Words to Help Students Understand 2-D and 3-D** Use words and expressions such as *flat* and *solid* or *on paper* and *the real object.* Students often explain that something that looks 3-D "pops out at you," "doesn't look flat," or "looks like you can hold it."

Math Note

❷ **What's the Goal?** The goal of this activity is not to improve drawing skills, although that will be the result for some students. Rather, the goal is for students to carefully observe and describe 3-D shapes as they try to represent them on paper.

ONGOING ASSESSMENT: Observing Students at Work

Students make a 2-D representation of a 3-D structure.

- **How do students approach the task?** Do they focus on one block at a time? The overall shape of the building? Do they draw each block? Do they draw only one face of each block or do they attempt to show, for example, that a particular block has square faces *and* rectangular faces? Can they show you which part of their drawing corresponds to which part of the building?

DIFFERENTIATION: Supporting the Range of Learners

You will find a wide range in students' drawings and explanations.❸

Intervention Encourage students who find the task overwhelming to break it into easier pieces by drawing just one of the blocks first. Ask them what shape(s) they see on that block and encourage them to draw what they see. As they move on to the second block, ask them how it relates to the first.

- Do the two blocks touch? Just a little bit or do they share a whole side? What shapes do you see on *this* block?

DISCUSSION
Drawing Geoblock Buildings

10 MIN   CLASS

Math Focus Points for Discussion

◆ Making a 2-D representation of a 3-D object or structure

When most students have completed their picture, ask them to share their work and to say what was easy or hard for them about drawing the building. Encourage them to describe what it is like to draw something that is three-dimensional on a flat surface and to explain what they did to try to make the object they were drawing look 3-D.

Record students' ideas on chart paper. For each idea draw an example next to it or ask the students to draw their own.

[Nicky] says that she drew a square and then she drew another square around it to make it look 3-D.

Nicky's Work

Teaching Note

❹ **2-D Pictures of 3-D Constructions** Show the class a book with illustrations of a variety of buildings. Good possibilities include *This is My House,* by Arthur Dorros; *Block City,* by Robert Louis Stevenson; *The Wonderful Towers of Watts,* by Patricia Zelver. You may also choose a David Macaulay book, such as *Castle, Cathedral, City,* or *Pyramid.*

[Toshi] says that if he could see more than one shape on a block, he tried to draw all of them. So when he drew this block [holds up triangular prism X], he drew a triangle first. What other shapes do you think [Toshi] saw on this block? [Toshi], can you come up and draw this block on our poster in case other students want to try your method?

Toshi's Work

If several students drew the same building from different angles, compare some of these drawings and ask students to comment on why drawings of the same building look different.

As you look at the pictures together, discuss what the artists did to make the pictures look 3-D.❹

Teaching Note

⑤ Students Should Use Representations That Make Sense to Them Ways to Draw Blocks (M20) shows conventional 2-D representations of several 3-D shapes. Although some students enjoy trying to draw shapes in this way, these representations are not meant to substitute for students' own ways of making shapes look 3-D.

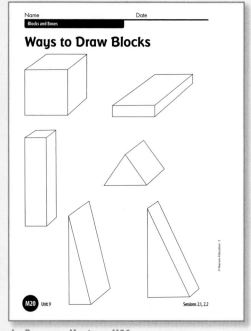

▲ Resource Masters, M20

30 MIN INDIVIDUALS

ACTIVITY

③ Building and Drawing

Near the chart that you have just created, post an enlarged (if possible) copy of Ways to Draw Blocks (M20) and explain that it shows how some people draw blocks to make them look three-dimensional. Explain that copies of the sheet will be available as they continue to draw 2-D representations of 3-D shapes over the course of this investigation.⑤

Explain to students that they will use three or four Geoblocks to construct a building and then draw what they have built. Emphasize that, although students may want to try the drawing approach shown on the poster, they can still draw their own way or try out one of the methods suggested by their classmates.

ONGOING ASSESSMENT: Observing Students at Work

Students build a 3-D structure and then represent it in two dimensions.

● **How do students approach the task?** Do they focus on one block at a time? The overall shape of the building? Do they draw each block? Do they draw only one face of each block or do they attempt to show, for example, that a particular block has square faces *and* rectangular faces? Can they show you which part of their drawing corresponds to which part of the building?

● **Are students using the examples on the chart from the previous discussion and the examples on M20 as a reference?**

A student draws a 2-D representation of the 3-D building she has created.

DIFFERENTIATION: Supporting the Range of Learners

Intervention Ask questions that help students think about how their drawings represent the different parts of the block building.

- How were you looking at the building when you drew this?

- Which part of the building does this part of your drawing show?

Help students revise their drawings to take into account what they can see about the objects they are drawing. ⑥

Extension Some students may have time to build and draw more than one construction. They may want to try a slightly larger building, using 6 to 8 blocks.

SESSION FOLLOW-UP
④ Daily Practice and Homework

 Daily Practice: For ongoing review, have students complete *Student Activity Book* page 14.

 Homework: On *Student Activity Book* page 15, students draw a picture of a building they have seen, either in their own neighborhood or somewhere they have visited. Students may also cut out a picture of a building and fasten it onto the page. They should write one or two sentences about the building.

 Student Math Handbook: Students and families may use *Student Math Handbook* page 84 for reference and review. See pages 124–126 in the back of this unit.

Professional Development

⑥ **Dialogue Box:** Making It Look 3-D, p. 121

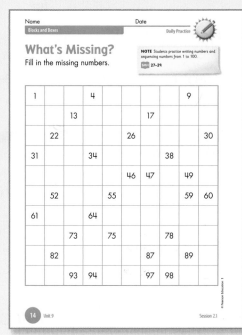

▲ Student Activity Book, p. 14

▲ Student Activity Book, p. 15

Building from a Plan

Math Focus Points

◆ Observing and describing characteristics of 3-D shapes

◆ Making a 2-D representation of a 3-D object or structure

◆ Building a 3-D construction from a 2-D representation

Today's Plan		Materials
ACTIVITY **❶ More Building and Drawing**	30 MIN INDIVIDUALS	• Materials from Session 2.1, p. 68
DISCUSSION **❷ Building from Pictures**	15 MIN CLASS	
ACTIVITY **❸ Even More Building and Drawing**	15 MIN INDIVIDUALS	• Materials from Session 2.1, p. 68
SESSION FOLLOW-UP **❹ Daily Practice**		• *Student Activity Book,* p. 17 • *Student Math Handbook,* pp. 84, 91 • M21–M22, Family Letter*

*See *Materials to Prepare,* p. 65.

Classroom Routines

Morning Meeting: Can Everyone Have a Partner? **Follow your daily** *Morning Meeting* **Routine. During** *Attendance,* **ask students to determine whether everyone can have a partner. Ask students to share their strategies.**

ACTIVITY

More Building and Drawing

30 MIN INDIVIDUALS

As they did in Session 2.1, each student builds a Geoblock construction, this time using no more than 6 to 10 blocks. (This limit is important to keep the task manageable.) Then, each student draws a picture of his or her own construction.

Try to make the clearest picture you can so that someone could easily recognize your building from it. This is something that architects do when they draw plans for a new building.

Math Note

❶ **What's the Goal?** The goal of this activity is for students to do the best they can to reproduce the 3-D construction represented in the drawing. Because some drawings will be easier to follow than others, the emphasis should be not on how well the construction matches the original building but on how well it follows what the drawing seems to show.

Students build a 3-D block structure and draw a 2-D plan.

Let students know that they have 15 minutes to build and draw. A strict time limit helps students focus on the drawing task rather than making elaborate or complicated buildings.

Remind students to refer to the chart and Ways to Draw Blocks (M20), as needed, to help them find ways to draw shapes in ways that look three-dimensional.

Ask students to disassemble their buildings.❶ Collect all the drawings, mix them up, and give out one drawing at random to each student. Make sure that no student gets his or her own drawing back.

Now you're going to try to build a construction from a picture as if you were building from a plan.

Give students about 15 minutes to complete their constructions.

ONGOING ASSESSMENT: Observing Students at Work

Students build 3-D structures and then represent them in two dimensions. They also build 3-D structures based on 2-D representations.

- **How do students approach the task of drawing their own building?** Do they focus on one block at a time? The overall shape of the building? Do they draw each block? Do they draw only one face of each block or do they attempt to show, for example, that a particular block has square faces *and* rectangular faces? Can they show you which part of their drawing corresponds to which part of the building?

- **Are students' drawings beginning to include more geometric features?**

- **How do students approach the task of building from another student's plan?** Do they choose blocks according to the shapes they see in the picture? How do they choose a block when a shape is not clear? Do their final buildings resemble the drawing?

DIFFERENTIATION: Supporting the Range of Learners

Intervention Encourage students who find the task of drawing a building overwhelming to draw one block at a time and to focus on the shapes they see in order to determine how those shapes connect to the ones they have already drawn. Continue to ask questions that help students think about how their drawings represent the different parts of the block building.

- **How were you looking at the building when you drew this?**

- **Which part of the building does this part of your drawing show?**

Help students revise their drawings to take into account what they can see about the objects they are drawing.

Intervention Some students may find parts of a plan difficult to follow. For example, they may not be sure which of two similarly shaped blocks is intended. Tell them to make the best choice they can, using whatever clues the plan gives them.

When most students have completed the building shown in the picture, ask them to place the picture next to their construction. Then, students walk around the room and compare the buildings and drawings.

② Building from Pictures

15 MIN   **CLASS**

Math Focus Points for Discussion

◆ Building a 3-D construction from a 2-D representation

After students have finished building from a plan, spend some time talking with them about what was difficult and not so difficult about following the plans and how they coped with parts of the plan they could not understand. Here are some examples of problems that students may have encountered and how they may have coped:

Paul could not find one of the blocks in the drawing, so he chose a substitute that was about the right size and shape.

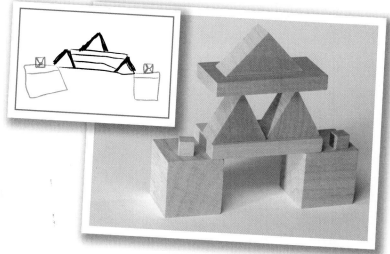

Stacy adjusted the base to make it more stable because it kept falling over.

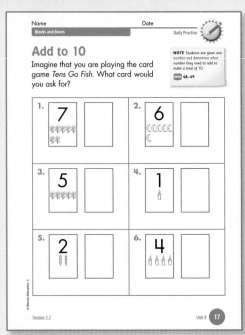

▲ **Student Activity Book, p. 17**

ACTIVITY

15 MIN **INDIVIDUALS**

3 Even More Building and Drawing

For details about this activity, see Session 1.2, p. 72.

Students should use this time to practice building and drawing. While students work, notice whether they address the problems that came up when they tried to build from one of their classmate's plans and whether they use any of the ideas that were brought up in the discussion.

SESSION FOLLOW-UP

4 Daily Practice

Daily Practice: For ongoing review, have students complete *Student Activity Book* page 17.

Student Math Handbook: Students and families may use *Student Math Handbook* pages 84, 91 for reference and review. See pages 124–126 in the back of this unit.

Family Letter: Send home copies of the Family Letter (M21–M22).

Buildings for Our Town

Math Focus Points

◆ Recognizing shapes in the world

◆ Planning a geometric structure with limited space and materials

◆ Making a 2-D representation of a 3-D object or structure

Today's Plan		Materials
① DISCUSSION **What Buildings Have You Seen?** 10 MIN CLASS		• *Student Activity Book,* p. 15 (from Session 2.1)
② DISCUSSION **What Buildings Do We Need?** 10 MIN CLASS		• Large street grid*; chart paper
③ ACTIVITY **Designing Buildings for Our Town** 40 MIN PAIRS		• Geoblocks (4 subsets); 5″ x 8″ index cards or half-sheets of $8\frac{1}{2}$″ x 11″ paper; markers or crayons; children's books about unusual buildings or houses (optional); shapes with curved sides (optional; from Session 2.1)
④ SESSION FOLLOW-UP **Daily Practice**		• *Student Activity Book,* p. 18 • *Student Math Handbook,* pp. 83, 84, 91

*See *Materials to Prepare,* p. 65.

Classroom Routines

Quick Survey: Consonant or Vowel? On chart paper, create a horizontal table titled "Does your name start with a consonant or a vowel?" with the headings "Consonant" and "Vowel (A, E, I, O, or U)" written at the left of each row. Use tally marks to record students' responses and then count them by 5s and 1s. Briefly discuss the results, being sure to note that the number of tallies is the same as the number of students in the class.

❶ **Using Children's Literature** If you have books about houses in other cultures or other interesting buildings, share them during this session or at other times of the day. Good possibilities include *My Painted House, My Friendly Chicken, and Me,* by Maya Angelou; *This Is My House,* by Arthur Dorros; *Round Buildings, Square Buildings, and Buildings that Wiggle Like a Fish,* by Phillip Isaacson; *Houses and Homes Around the World,* by Josephine Karavasil; *Houses and Homes,* by Ann Morris.

DISCUSSION

What Buildings Have You Seen?

10 MIN   CLASS

Math Focus Points for Discussion

◆ Recognizing shapes in the world

Ask students to share some of the buildings they drew or pasted for homework onto *Student Activity Book* page 15.

Sample Student Work

Ask questions that help students focus on the shapes and parts of the buildings in their neighborhood, town, or elsewhere.❶

When you looked at buildings in your neighborhood, what shapes did you notice?

What shapes were the buildings? Did you see a building that reminded you of any of the Geoblocks?

What are the roofs around your neighborhood like? Are there different kinds of roofs? Did you see a roof that reminded you of any of the Geoblocks?

What unusual building have you seen? What shape was it?

DISCUSSION

What Buildings Do We Need?

10 MIN   CLASS

Math Focus Points for Discussion

◆ Planning a geometric structure with limited space and materials

After discussing the kinds of buildings students have seen in their neighborhoods, show them the large grid of streets you made from Street Grid (M23)❷ and explain that as a class, you will be building a town of your own. Brainstorm with students what kinds of buildings they may like to have in their town. Make a list of their ideas on the board or on chart paper, perhaps adding simple pictures to symbolize the written words. The following is a list from one first grade class:

	Buildings for Our Town	
houses	apartment building	grocery station
school	police station	toy store
pet shop	museum	ice cream store
veterinarian	zoo	restaurant
parking lot	pool	hotel
skating rink	arcade	auto repair shop
library	shelter	clothing store
stadium	fire station	gas station

Use this discussion to help students think about the buildings that are around them and their functions. Ask students to think about all of the needs of a town.

What type of buildings do we need to have in our town?

If students mention very specific buildings, such as a specific fast-food restaurant or grocery store, you may want to ask them to name the general category for that building (e.g., restaurant or supermarket). This exercise also gives students a chance to explore vocabulary about the types of businesses housed in the town buildings.❸

Is there a difference between a grocery store and a supermarket? What is a hardware store?

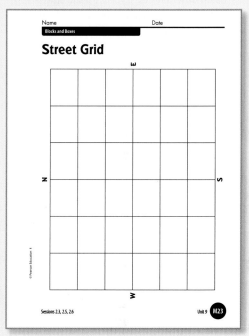

▲ **Resource Masters, M23**

Math Note

④ **Why Limit the Blocks?** Limiting the number of blocks is intended to help students keep their buildings a manageable size so that they can draw clear plans and successfully rebuild their buildings on the large town grid.

Teaching Note

⑤ **Using Other Blocks** If you are using other sets of building blocks along with the Geoblocks, you will need to assign pairs of students to different sets of blocks or have a system for borrowing the shapes with curved sides, such as cylinders and cones, from the other sets.

DIFFERENTIATION: Supporting the Range of Learners

ELL English Language Learners may need to spend some time reviewing relevant English vocabulary in order to participate in this discussion. While they might already know words such as *house, store,* and *restaurant,* more subtle terms, such as *supermarket* and *hardware store,* may require additional explanation. Most ESL picture dictionaries include sections about community buildings. These would be good resources for English Language Learners to draw upon before this discussion and throughout the following activities.

ACTIVITY

40 MIN   PAIRS

③ Designing Buildings for Our Town

Pairs look at the chart and choose a building to design for the class town.

Give each pair one 5″ x 8″ index card or a half-sheet of paper. Explain that this is the amount of land they have on which to build. Each building must fit entirely on the card or paper and use no more than 12 blocks.④ ⑤

Explain that today students will design and build a building and then draw a plan for it on a separate sheet of paper (*not* on the card or paper that represents your land). Tomorrow, they will use their plans to rebuild their building on the street grid. Emphasize that they will need to draw their plans carefully so that it will help them remember.

ONGOING ASSESSMENT: Observing Students at Work

Students build 3-D structures and then represent them in two dimensions.

- **How do students design their building, given the limitations on space and the number of blocks they can use?**

- **How do students draw a 2-D plan of their building?** Do they focus on one block at a time? The overall shape of the building? Do they draw each block? Do they draw only one face of each block or do they attempt to show, for example, that a particular block has square faces *and* rectangular faces? Can they show you which part of their drawing corresponds to which part of the building?

Students compare a block building with the plan they have created for it.

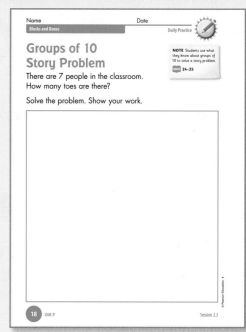

▲ **Student Activity Book, p. 18**

DIFFERENTIATION: Supporting the Range of Learners

Intervention Encourage students who find the task of drawing their structure overwhelming to draw one block at a time and to focus on the shapes that they see and on how those shapes connect to the ones they have already drawn. Continue to ask questions that help students think about how their drawings represent the different parts of the block building.

● Where were you standing when you drew this? Which part of the building does this part of your drawing show?

Help students revise their drawings to take into account what they can see about the objects they are drawing.

SESSION FOLLOW-UP

4 Daily Practice

 Daily Practice: For ongoing review, have students complete *Student Activity Book* page 18.

 Student Math Handbook: Students and families may use *Student Math Handbook* pages 83, 84, 91 for reference and review. See pages 124–126 in the back of this unit.

Building Our Town

Math Focus Points

◆ Making a 2-D representation of a 3-D object or structure

◆ Building a 3-D construction from a 2-D representation

◆ Describing 3-D structures

Today's Plan		Materials
① ACTIVITY **Introducing Describing Our Buildings and Building Our Buildings**	10 MIN CLASS	• M24*
② MATH WORKSHOP **Building Our Town** **2A** Designing Buildings for Our Town **2B** Describing Our Buildings **2C** Building Our Buildings	50 MIN	**2A** • Materials from Session 2.3, p. 79 **2B** • M24* • Students' plans (from Session 2.3 and the previous Math Workshop Activity 2A) **2C** • Materials from Session 2.3, p. 79 • Students' plans (from Session 2.3 and Math Workshop Activity 2A)
③ SESSION FOLLOW-UP **Daily Practice**		• *Student Activity Book,* p. 19 • *Student Math Handbook,* pp. 85, 91

*See *Materials to Prepare,* p. 65.

Classroom Routines

Tell a Story Write "9 + 8 =" on chart paper. Ask students to suggest a story problem. After several students have shared ideas, have students solve the problem. If time permits, repeat with "17 − 10 =".

10 MIN   CLASS

① Introducing Describing Our Buildings and Building Our Buildings

Spend a few minutes at the beginning of this session discussing names for the class town. Make a list of suggestions and keep it posted. You do not need to come to a conclusion as a class now.

Ask students to think about names as they build the town today. Add any new ideas to the list as they come up during Math Workshop. The class will decide on a name in the next session.

Explain to students that during this session they will be writing about the building that they created on Describing My Building (M24). Their writing should include the name of the building, what it is used for, and a list of the shapes that can be seen when looking at it.

Then, explain that as they are writing about their buildings, you will be asking pairs to bring their plans to the large street grid to assemble them.

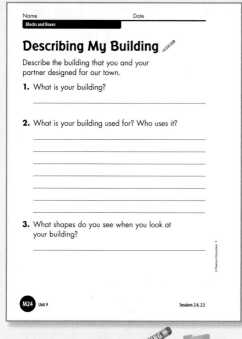

Name _____ Date _____
Blocks and Boxes

Describing My Building
Describe the building that you and your partner designed for our town.

1. What is your building?
   _____

2. What is your building used for? Who uses it?
   _____
   _____
   _____
   _____
   _____

3. What shapes do you see when you look at your building?
   _____

M24 Unit 9   Sessions 2.4, 2.5

▲ Resource Masters, M24

50 MIN

② Building Our Town

Pairs who have not finished drawing a plan should begin with the Designing Buildings for Our Town activity. Give them a time limit, if necessary, so that they will have time to complete the other activities.

All students should at least begin describing their buildings in writing during this Math Workshop.

2A Designing Buildings for Our Town

PAIRS

For complete details about this activity, see Session 2.3, page 82.

Teaching Notes

❶ **Displaying Students' Work** Post students' writing on Describing My Building (M24) and their building plans, side-by-side, near the town.

❷ **Managing the Building Process** To avoid knocking over one anothers' buildings, students should start building near the middle of the grid and work outward. If the town is set up against a wall, they can build from the wall outward. If possible, encourage students to leave a blank rectangle between their building and other buildings. If a building does get knocked down, remind students that this is why they have plans. The plans will help with repairs as needed.

❸ **Connections Across the Curriculum** As students erect their buildings, talk with them about where certain ones should go. Which buildings should be close to apartments or houses? Which can be farther away? For example, one class decided that the school should be close to the houses and apartments because that is where the children live, that the police station should be close to the museum in case there was a robbery, and that the zoo should be far away from the library because it is too noisy.

2B Describing Our Buildings

INDIVIDUALS

Students write about the buildings that they designed for the class town with a partner on Describing My Building (M24). They should include the building's name, what it is used for, and what shapes can be seen when looking at it.❶

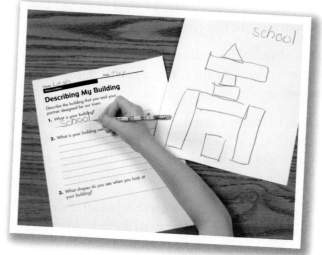

A student works on Describing My Building (M24).

ONGOING ASSESSMENT: Observing Students at Work

Students write about the buildings that they have designed, drawn, and built.

- **Can students name the kind of building they made?**
  Do they know who and what their building is designed for?

- **Can they name or draw the shapes that can be seen in their building?**

2C Building Our Buildings

PAIRS

Pairs bring the plan of their building to the area where the large street grid is located. Help pairs select one of the rectangles on the grid as a site for their building.❷ Also, allow each pair to name one of the streets. Write the names they choose along the lines of the grid.❸

Because you will be duplicating small grids of your finished town with the location of each building marked, you may want to have students make a sign for their buildings. This way you will be able to identify each one (e.g., Emilia and Diego's house, Sacha and Neil's pet store, the Sears Tower, and so on).

Students use their 2-D plan to build a 3-D structure.

Students may also enjoy adding details such as paper or cardboard trees, windows, or signs, as well as small toy figures of people, animals, or cars (if available).

ONGOING ASSESSMENT: Observing Students at Work

As students build a 3-D structure based on a 2-D plan, they notice, describe, and compare 3-D objects.

- **Do students notice that some Geoblocks have only rectangular faces and that some have triangular faces?** Do they distinguish between these in their drawing?

- **Do students notice that Geoblocks that are somewhat alike in shape can be distinguished by comparing dimensions (size and thickness)?** In students' drawings and buildings, do they distinguish, for example, between a large cube and a smaller cube or describe one rectangular prism as much thinner than another?

- **Do students see that some 3-D objects have faces that are different shapes; for example, two triangular faces and three rectangular faces?** Can you tell from their drawings—and the way they match their buildings to their drawings—that they are aware of the variety of faces a single block may have?

Missing Numbers 2
Write the missing numbers on the counting strips.

NOTE Students practice counting, writing, and sequencing numbers.
SMH 21–23, 31

15	23	75	97
16	24	76	98
17	25	77	99

Session 2.4   Unit 9   19

▲ **Student Activity Book, p. 19**

A student adds his building to the class town.

As students place their buildings, ask them how they can tell from their plans which blocks go where.

How do you know that this size cube goes here instead of a smaller cube?

How did you know from your plan that this block goes here?

These activities combine a wide variety of skills, some that are mathematical and some that are not. Remember that you are not assessing students on how good their drawings are or on how well their buildings match their drawings. The focus instead should be on how well students are describing and comparing different 3-D shapes.

SESSION FOLLOW-UP

3 Daily Practice

 Daily Practice: For ongoing review, have students complete *Student Activity Book* page 19.

 Student Math Handbook: Students and families may use *Student Math Handbook* pages 85, 91 for reference and review. See pages 124–126 in the back of this unit.

Building Our Town, *continued*

Math Focus Points

◆ Building a 3-D construction from a 2-D representation

◆ Describing 3-D structures

Today's Plan		Materials
MATH WORKSHOP **1 Building Our Town** **1A** Describing Our Buildings **1B** Building Our Buildings	🕐 **55 MIN**	**1A** • M24 (from Session 2.4) • Students' plans (from Sessions 2.3 and 2.4) **1B** • M23 (from Session 2.3) • Materials from Session 2.4, p. 84
DISCUSSION **2 Naming Our Town**	🕐 **5 MIN** 👥 **CLASS**	• Class town
SESSION FOLLOW-UP **3 Daily Practice and Homework**		• *Student Activity Book,* pp. 20–21 • *Student Math Handbook,* pp. 85, 91

*See *Materials to Prepare,* p. 67.

Classroom Routines

Quick Images: Shapes Show transparencies from Shape Cards (T61–T63), beginning with Shape J. Follow the basic *Quick Images* activity. Ask students to describe the shape after they have drawn it. Repeat with Shape L and then Shape Q. Compare the three shapes at the end of the activity.

55 MIN

MATH WORKSHOP

Building Our Town

During this Math Workshop, all students should finish describing their building in writing on Describing My Building (M24). Also, pairs should finish assembling their buildings on the large street grid. Students who have finished both activities can choose a previous Math Workshop activity, such as Geoblock Footprints from Session 1.1, pages 24–25, Blocks in a Sock from Session 1.4, page 40, or Building and Drawing from Session 2.1, page 72.

1A Describing Our Buildings

INDIVIDUALS

For complete details about this activity, see Session 2.4, page 86.

1B Building Our Buildings

PAIRS

For complete details about this activity, see Session 2.4, pages 86–88 and consider the following notes.

When the town is complete, write the names of all of its buildings in the right locations on a copy of Street Grid (M23) and put a dot in the corners of their rectangles to indicate the entrance to each building. You will make a copy for each student to use in Sessions 2.6 and 2.7. See the Investigation Planner for Session 2.6 on page 67 for further instructions.

DISCUSSION

Naming Our Town

5 MIN   CLASS

When all of the buildings are in place, give students a chance to look at the whole town. Ask whether they have thought of any other ideas for naming the town and add any new names to the list. As a class, decide on a name for the town.

SESSION FOLLOW-UP

Daily Practice and Homework

 Daily Practice: For ongoing review, have students complete *Student Activity Book* page 20.

 Homework: Students circle the blocks that have faces that match the given footprints on *Student Activity Book* page 21.

 Student Math Handbook: Students and families may use *Student Math Handbook* pages 85, 91 for reference and review. See pages 124–126 in the back of this unit.

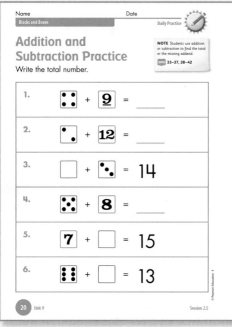

▲ Student Activity Book, p. 20

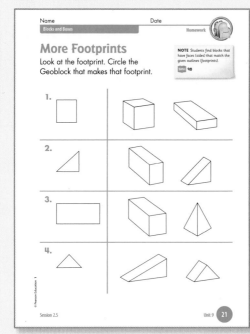

▲ Student Activity Book, p. 21

Giving Directions

Math Focus Points

◆ Visualizing and estimating the paces and turns required to follow a particular path

◆ Giving, following, and recording directions for following a path

Today's Plan		Materials
ACTIVITY **① Robot Paths in the Classroom**	15 MIN · CLASS	
ACTIVITY **② Introducing Paths Through Town**	15 MIN · CLASS	• T67 * • Toy person or car, small block or counter, or small cardboard pointer (1); chart paper
ACTIVITY **③ Paths Through Town**	30 MIN · PAIRS	• Map of the class town*; lined paper; toy people or cars, small blocks or counters, or small cardboard pointers
SESSION FOLLOW-UP **④ Daily Practice**		• Student Activity Book, p. 23 • Student Math Handbook, p. 92

*See Materials to Prepare, p. 67.

Classroom Routines

Quick Survey: Siblings? On chart paper, create a Venn diagram titled "Do you have older siblings, younger siblings, both, or neither?" Label the inside of the first circle "Older Siblings," the second circle "Younger Siblings," and the overlapping section "Both Older and Younger." Discuss with students where to list people who have no siblings (outside the circles). List students' names in the appropriate sections and count them. After counting the responses, briefly discuss the results of the survey.

ACTIVITY
Robot Paths in the Classroom

15 MIN   CLASS

In this activity, students will give you verbal directions for moving from one place to another. Choose a starting place and an ending place for a path in your classroom (e.g., from the door to your desk). To begin, choose a path that does not require more than one turn. Explain to students that you are going to act like a robot and that they are going to direct you.

I'm standing at the door and I want to walk to my desk. Remember, I'm a robot. I only know how to walk straight ahead and how to turn. What should I do first?

Ask volunteers to give you directions that will get you to your desk.

[Diego] thinks I should walk straight ahead. How many paces do you think I should go?

Explain that a pace is a normal walking step—not a giant step or a baby step, just an ordinary step.

Try out students' directions. If a student suggests six paces, go six paces and stop. Then, ask for the next direction. If a student tells you to go too many paces, keep going so the class can see where they take you. Then, go back to your starting point and ask for another estimate. Point out that they now have some information to use.

So, ten paces is too many because it takes me past where I need to go. That's good information for making a new estimate. How many paces should I go instead?

When it is time to make a turn, ask students which way you should turn.❶

*OK, I'm at [Keena's] desk. Now what? What do I have to do to get to my desk?*❷

Note that in Grade 1, students are not expected to specify *how far* to turn in terms of degrees. (This concept is introduced in Grade 2.) If students use a landmark in the classroom, how much to turn is not an issue because you will be turning to "face the sink." If they use the "turn right" or "turn left" method, 90° (a quarter of a full rotation) is a convenient amount for each turn. Students may then need to say "turn right" or "turn left" more than once to get you to face in the intended direction.

Teaching Note

❶ **Right or Left?** This is a good opportunity to review right and left. Note that students who can tell their own right and left may not be able to tell another person's. This requires visualizing oneself in another's position, which can be difficult even for adults.

Math Note

❷ **Helping Students with Turns** Tell students to use landmarks in the classroom to help give directions that involve turns. For example, turn toward the chalkboard, sink, or bookshelf. You may also hold a piece of paper labeled R in your right hand and one labeled L in your left hand. Students can tell you whether to turn toward your right hand or your left hand. Introduce both methods so that students can use the one that is easier for them.

Teaching Note

❸ **Robot Paces in Bigger Spaces** If you have access to a large space, such as a gymnasium or outside area, have students play Robot Paths in pairs. Set up folding chairs, pylons, or other large objects with numbers on them for students to use as starting and ending points. One student is the robot, while the other gives directions.

Continue asking students to give you directions until you have reached the destination you indicated.

OK, I've turned as far as you told me to go. Am I ready to walk straight ahead again now? Who can tell me how many paces I should go?

Students need not give you the whole distance at once. For example, they could try three or four paces, see how far you are, and then tell you the next distance.

When you have reached your destination, choose new starting and ending points and repeat the activity.

Then, ask one or two student volunteers to be the robot. This time, have a student in the class pick a starting and ending point and give directions to the student robot. Ask the student to walk across the classroom first so that the class can get an idea of how long this new "robot's" paces are. They may notice that the student's paces are shorter than yours were. ❸

Students direct a robot volunteer on a path through the classroom.

DIFFERENTIATION: Supporting the Range of Learners

ELL English Language Learners may need to review terminology such as *right, left, straight,* and *forward* in order to participate in the activities in Sessions 2.6 and 2.7. It might be helpful to meet separately with these students during Math Workshop. Begin by demonstrating a set of very simple directions: Listen to what I say, and watch what I do. First, I'm taking three steps *forward*. Now I'm turning *left*. Now I'm taking two more steps *straight ahead*. Where am I? Repeat the exercise with another set of directions. Then have English Language Learners take turns following directions given by you. Finally, have the students practice their oral language skills by giving directions to you or to each other.

ACTIVITY

2 Introducing Paths Through Town

15 MIN   CLASS

Display the transparency of the map of the class town that you created.

		N			
Vet ■					
	Apartment House ■	Fire Station ■	Police ■		
	Park with pool ■	School ■			
W	Pet Shop ■		Bank	Parking Lot ■	Pizza ■	E
			Used Cars ■		
Movies ■		Zoo ■			Hospital ■
		S			

Explain that you filled in this grid so that it would represent your class town. Orient students to the map by comparing the placement of several buildings in the class town with the corresponding location on the map.

This blank grid has the same number of squares as our town. To make a map of our town, I looked at where each building was in our town and wrote it in on this grid. In [Capital City], the vet's office was way up here [points to the top left square of the town]. So, on my map, I put the vet's office here [points to the top left square on the map], in the same block that it is on in our town.

Show students your "traveler," the toy person, car, or small block you collected. Explain that students will direct your "traveler" to different locations on the map. Before beginning, discuss with students how they will know which way the "traveler" is facing. If you select a small toy person, car, or a teddy bear counter as the "traveler," it will be clear which direction it is facing. If you use a small block or counter, you can attach an arrow or simply use a cardboard pointer to indicate which way is front.

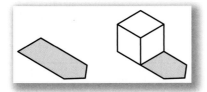

Just as you did for Robot Paths, choose a starting and an ending place in the town. Explain that the dot at the corner of each building indicates the entrance. A path should always start and end at a dot. Put the "traveler" at the starting place (a dot) and ask students to give directions to move it to the chosen destination. Instead of suggesting the number of paces, remind students that they will be indicating the number of blocks that the "traveler" should move.

For this activity, you're going to suggest how many city blocks to go, instead of paces.

Like the robot, the "traveler" on the map can either go straight ahead for a specified number of blocks or turn.

Students can use the north (N), south (S), east (E), and west (W) markings on the sheet to indicate the direction of the turn they want. Students at this age are not expected to understand compass directions; these are just convenient labels.

After completing one trip through the town with the "traveler," choose another starting and ending location. This time, as students give directions, record the directions in a list. Do this once or twice.

START: Pet Shop

Turn east

Go forward 1 block

Turn north

Go forward 2 blocks

Turn east

Go forward 1 block

END: Fire station

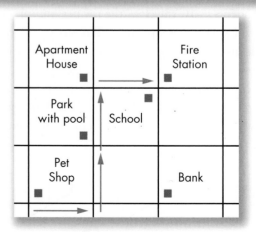

Can you think of a shorter way to write the directions? Can you make up a code that would be easy to write?

Students may suggest using F for forward, B for block, and N, S, W, and E for turns, producing the following:

E F1B N F2B E F1B

They might suggest using arrows:

→ F1B ↑ F2B → F1B

One class decided to use T for turn:

TE 1B TN 2B TE 1B

Any code that everyone agrees on is fine. Use the code to help students distinguish between the action of turning while staying in one location and the action of moving forward to a new location.

ACTIVITY

30 MIN PAIRS

3 Paths Through Town

After the class has established a code and recorded a couple of trips together, give a copy of the map of your class town to each pair, along with a sheet of lined paper and a "traveler."

Using the class code, you're going to work together to take and record different trips around the town. Remember to decide on your starting and ending points before you start your trip.

One way to explain how students are to record their work is to set up a model structure on the board.

Start: _____

_____

_____

_____

_____

End: _____

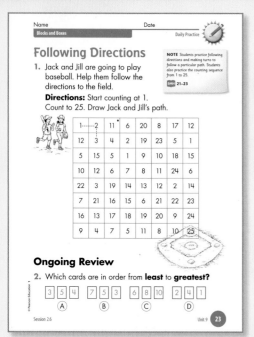

▲ **Student Activity Book, p. 23**

ONGOING ASSESSMENT: Observing Students at Work

Students visualize paths, give directions to get a traveler from one point to another, and use a code to record their directions.

- **How do students plot a trip from Point A to Point B?** Do they stay on roads and turn at intersections? Do they plan the most direct trip or trips that go all over town? How comfortable are they with complicated trips that involve many turns?

- **How do students use the class code to record trips?**

- **In planning and recording trips, can students distinguish between the action of turning while staying in one location and the action of moving forward to a new location?**

Do not expect students to be completely consistent in using the class code to record their trips. Some students will have difficulty separating turns from forward movement. For example, Nicky uses 2B to show a forward movement of two blocks, but she also uses a direction to show forward movement (e.g., 1E means one block east). Sometimes she combines these (e.g., 1BE also means one block east). Despite these inconsistencies, Nicky carefully plans her trip and records directions. She successfully creates a path from one location to another.

Nicky's Work

SESSION FOLLOW-UP

Daily Practice

Daily Practice: For reinforcement of this unit's content, have students complete *Student Activity Book* page 23.

Student Math Handbook: Students and families may use *Student Math Handbook* page 92 for reference and review. See pages 124–126 in the back of this unit.

Giving Directions, *continued*

Math Focus Points

◆ Visualizing and estimating the paces and turns required to follow a particular path

◆ Giving, following, and recording directions for following a path

◆ Counting and adding to compare the distances of different paths

Today's Plan		Materials
① ACTIVITY **Long Paths and Short Paths**	🕐 👥 15 MIN CLASS	
② MATH WORKSHOP **Trips on Grids** **2A** Where Are You? **2B** Paths Through Town	🕐 45 MIN	**2A** • *Student Activity Book,* pp. 24–27 • Toy people or cars, small blocks or counters, or small cardboard pointers **2B** • Materials from Session 2.6, p. 92.
③ SESSION FOLLOW-UP **Daily Practice and Homework**		• *Student Activity Book,* pp. 28–29 • *Student Math Handbook,* p. 92

Classroom Routines

Tell a Story Write "10 + 3 =" on chart paper. Ask students to suggest a story problem. After several students have shared ideas, have students solve the problem. If time permits, repeat with "6 + 7 =".

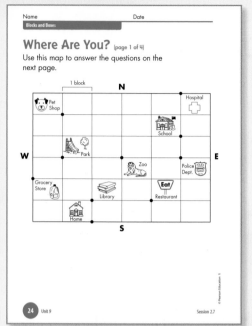

Student Activity Book, p. 24 PORTFOLIO

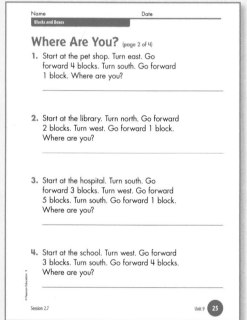

Student Activity Book, p. 25 PORTFOLIO

ACTIVITY

15 MIN   CLASS

1 Long Paths and Short Paths

Begin this session with the Robot Path activity you did at the start of Session 2.6. Ask a volunteer to be the robot. This time, ask students to think about long paths and short paths.

Pick a starting point and an ending point. Challenge students to look for the shortest possible path. As the student robot follows the directions, record on the board the number of paces and turns the robot takes.

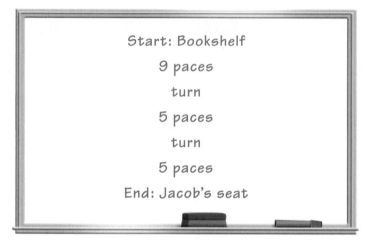

Start: Bookshelf

9 paces

turn

5 paces

turn

5 paces

End: Jacob's seat

How many paces did our robot move on the whole path? How did you figure this out?

Students might say:

"I know 5 and 5 is 10 and then I counted up 9 more."

"I know 9 and 5 is 14 because I put 1 on the 9 and that's 10, and then 4 more is 14. Then I counted up 5 more."

"I did 5 and 5 is 10 and then I just knew that 10 and 9 is 19."

Next, students give the student robot directions to take a longer path from the same starting point to the same ending point.

Before, the robot was in a hurry and wanted to take the shortest path possible. Now we're going to give our robot directions from the bookshelf to [Jacob's] seat again, but this time the robot is not in a hurry, so it can take a longer path.

Again, record the students' directions and ask them to figure out how many paces the robot took. Repeat this activity once or twice with a different robot each time.

MATH WORKSHOP

② Trips on Grids

45 MIN

Take a minute to introduce *Student Activity Book* pages 24–25. Explain that this is one of two activities that students can choose to work on today.

②A Where Are You?

INDIVIDUALS

On *Student Activity Book* pages 24–27, students are given a map of a town, a starting point, and several directions. They will need to use this information to figure out the ending point.

ONGOING ASSESSMENT: Observing Students at Work

Students follow the directions on the map of a town.

- **Can students follow directions?** Do they travel in the right direction? Do they go the right number of blocks? How do they handle directions about turning? Do they end at the intended destination?

DIFFERENTIATION: Supporting the Range of Learners

Intervention If students are having difficulty following the set of move-and-turn directions, encourage students to use a "traveler" and to deal with just one direction at a time.

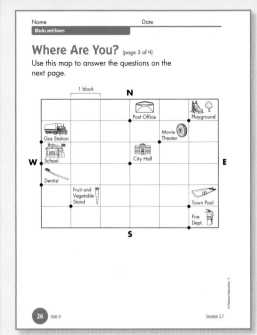

▲ **Student Activity Book, p. 26**

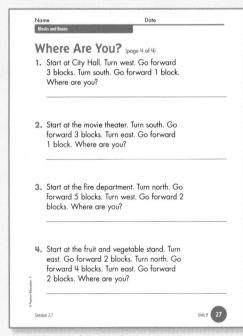

▲ **Student Activity Book, p. 27**

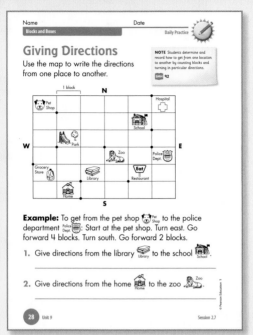

▲ Student Activity Book, p. 28

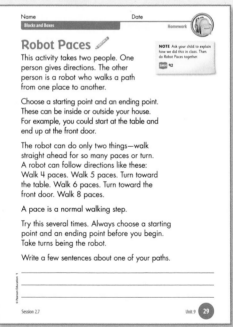

▲ Student Activity Book, p. 29

2B Paths Through Town

PAIRS

For complete details about this activity, see Session 2.6, pages 95–98 and consider the following note.

DIFFERENTIATION: Supporting the Range of Learners

Extension If students have done two or three paths, ask them to find a long path and a very short path between two locations on the grid.

SESSION FOLLOW-UP

3 Daily Practice and Homework

Daily Practice: For reinforcement of this unit's content, have students complete *Student Activity Book* page 28.

Homework: Students do the Robot Paces activity at home with a family member as a partner. On *Student Activity Book* page 29, they record—in any way they choose—one of the paths that they followed.

Student Math Handbook: Students and families may use *Student Math Handbook* page 92 for reference and review. See pages 124–126 in the back of this unit.

End-of-Unit Assessment

Math Focus Points

◆ Making a 2-D representation of a 3-D object or structure

Today's Plan		Materials
ASSESSMENT ACTIVITY **①** End-of-Unit Assessment: Matching Plans to Buildings	✓ 60 MIN INDIVIDUALS	• M25; M26* • 4 Geoblock buildings with letter labels*; Geoblocks
SESSION FOLLOW-UP **②** Daily Practice		• *Student Activity Book,* p. 31 • *Student Math Handbook,* pp. 85, 86, 90, 91

*See *Materials to Prepare,* p. 67.

Classroom Routines

Morning Meeting: Discussing the Yearly Data Follow your daily *Morning Meeting* Routine. During *Weather,* discuss the data that has been collected for the year. Choose a few categories and ask students to look at the data collected.

How many days has it [rained] this year? How do you know?

Have students share their strategies.

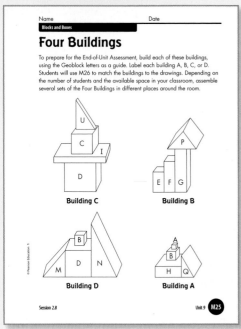

Name _____ Date _____
Blocks and Boxes

Four Buildings

To prepare for the End-of-Unit Assessment, build each of these buildings, using the Geoblock letters as a guide. Label each building A, B, C, or D. Students will use M26 to match the buildings to the drawings. Depending on the number of students and the available space in your classroom, assemble several sets of the Four Buildings in different places around the room.

Building C   Building B

Building D   Building A

Session 2.8   Unit 9 **M25**

▲ Resource Masters, M25

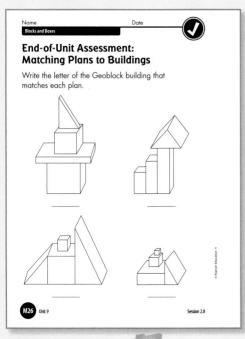

Name _____ Date _____
Blocks and Boxes ✓

End-of-Unit Assessment: Matching Plans to Buildings

Write the letter of the Geoblock building that matches each plan.

M26 Unit 9   Session 2.8

▲ Resource Masters, M26

ASSESSMENT ACTIVITY

① End-of-Unit Assessment: Matching Plans to Buildings

60 MIN   INDIVIDUALS

Geoblock Buildings for End-of-Unit Assessment

This assessment addresses Benchmark 2: Match a 2-D representation to a 3-D shape or structure. Watching and talking with students as they complete this sheet will also provide information about Benchmark 1: Attend to features of 3-D shapes, such as overall size and shape, the number and shape of faces, and the number of corners.

For the last few weeks, we've been looking very closely at the Geoblocks. You've been using them to construct buildings for our town and you've been working on how to draw something that's real, or three-dimensional, in two dimensions on paper. You've built Geoblock buildings, drawn and revised plans for building a Geoblock building, and used a plan to build a building.

Explain that today students will work individually so that you can see how much each student has grown in his or her ability to identify, describe, and compare 2-D and 3-D shapes. Show students a set of the four Geoblock buildings.

I've made four different Geoblock buildings: Building A, Building B, Building C, and Building D.

Point out the different places in the room where you have built a set of these four buildings. Explain that each set contains the same buildings.

You're going to get a sheet that has drawings of my four buildings. We've been talking about these types of drawings as plans for making buildings. Your job is to decide which plan goes with which building.

Hand out End-of-Unit Assessment: Matching Plans to Buildings (M26) and explain how students will write the letter of the building beneath its matching plan or drawing. Send four to six students at a time to each station you have set up.

 Teacher Note: End-of-Unit Assessment: Matching Plans to Buildings, p. 115

Students match plans to buildings.

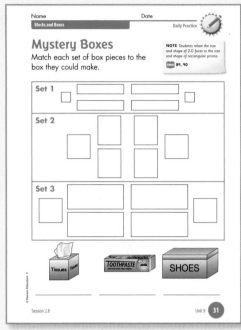

▲ **Student Activity Book, p. 31**

When students have finished, they can draw one of the buildings on the back of the sheet, use one of the plans to build a building, or choose any of the Math Workshop activities from this unit.

ONGOING ASSESSMENT: Observing Students at Work

Observe students as they match 2-D representations to 3-D structures.

- **Can students accurately match the 2-D representations to the 3-D buildings?** What features do they focus on? How do they explain how they know whether or not a plan matches a building?

SESSION FOLLOW-UP

2 Daily Practice

 Daily Practice: For enrichment, have students complete *Student Activity Book* page 31.

Student Math Handbook: Students and families may use *Student Math Handbook* pages 85, 86, 90, 91 for reference and review. See pages 124–126 in the back of this unit.

Types of 3-D Shapes

Students will have their own informal ways of naming and describing the 3-D shapes that they encounter. For example, they may call a cube a "box" or a sphere a "ball." They will also use the names of 2-D shapes they know to describe 3-D shapes, calling a cube a "square" or a triangular prism a "triangle."

You can use the correct names for 3-D shapes so that students hear the terms, but you do not need to insist that they use them. It is more important that they focus on describing and comparing these shapes. 3-D shapes are divided into two major categories—polyhedra and nonpolyhedra. Polyhedra are shapes that have only flat faces. All of the blocks in the Geoblock set are polyhedra.

Students will also encounter in their environment and in other building sets shapes that are not polyhedra—such as spheres, cylinders, cones, and others.

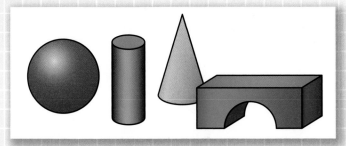

Polyhedra are sometimes classified by the number of faces they have. For example, a polyhedron with four faces is called a *tetrahedron,* while a polyhedron with eight faces is an *octahedron.* However, polyhedra are also classified another way; most of the blocks in the Geoblock set and

many of the common 3-D shapes you and your students see in everyday life are prisms.

Prisms are 3-D shapes that have two congruent faces connected by faces that are parallelograms. A prism is named by the two congruent faces.

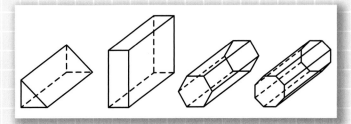

All of the shapes shown above are right prisms because faces that are rectangles connect the congruent faces. The first shape above is called a *triangular prism* because it has two faces that are triangles. These triangles are connected by faces that are rectangles. The second shape is called a *rectangular prism.* In a rectangular prism, all the faces are rectangles. The third shape is a *hexagonal prism.* The fourth is an *octagonal prism.*

The Geoblock set includes a variety of rectangular prisms, including cubes (rectangular prisms in which all of the faces are squares). The set also includes a variety of triangular prisms. Some students enjoy learning the names *triangular prism* and *rectangular prism.*

One shape in the Geoblock set is not a prism; it is a pyramid. A pyramid may have any polygon as its base. All of its other faces are triangles that connect at a single vertex. Like prisms, pyramids are named by the shapes of their bases. Here are a triangular pyramid, two square pyramids, and a pentagonal pyramid.

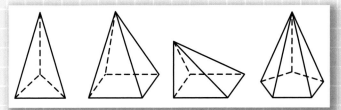

The third pyramid is like the one in the Geoblock set. A chart depicting all 25 different types of Geoblocks, and their quantities, appears below.

Cube A
1 cm × 1 cm × 1 cm
Quantity: 128

Rectangular prism H
2 cm × 4 cm × 4 cm
Quantity: 12

Triangular prism O
4 cm × 4 cm × 2 cm
Quantity: 12

Triangular prism U
4 cm × 8 cm × 1 cm
Quantity: 6

Cube B
2 cm × 2 cm × 2 cm
Quantity: 32

Rectangular prism I
1 cm × 8 cm × 4 cm
Quantity: 8

Triangular prism P
3 cm × 3 cm × 4 cm
Quantity: 8

Triangular prism V
2 cm × 4 cm × 2 cm
Quantity: 7

Cube C
3 cm × 3 cm × 3 cm
Quantity: 12

Rectangular prism J
2 cm × 8 cm × 4 cm
Quantity: 4

Triangular prism Q
2 cm × 4 cm × 4 cm
Quantity: 2

Triangular prism W
4 cm × 3.5 cm × 2 cm
Quantity: 6

Cube D
4 cm × 4 cm × 4 cm
Quantity: 8

Rectangular prism K
4 cm × 8 cm × 4 cm
Quantity: 2

Triangular prism R
4 cm × 8 cm × 2 cm
Quantity: 6

Triangular prism X
2 cm × 8 cm × 2 cm
Quantity: 6

Rectangular prism E
2 cm × 4 cm × 2 cm
Quantity: 8

Triangular prism L
2 cm × 2 cm × 2 cm
Quantity: 32

Triangular prism S
2 cm × 8 cm × 4 cm
Quantity: 6

Square pyramid Y
4 cm × 4 cm × 4 cm
Quantity: 6

Rectangular prism F
2 cm × 6 cm × 2 cm
Quantity: 4

Triangular prism M
4 cm × 4 cm × 4 cm
Quantity: 6

Triangular prism T
2 cm × 4 cm × 8 cm
Quantity: 6

Rectangular prism G
2 cm × 8 cm × 2 cm
Quantity: 4

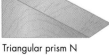

Triangular prism N
4 cm × 8 cm × 4 cm
Quantity: 2

Assessment: Matching Blocks to Outlines

Problem: 1

Benchmark addressed:

Benchmark 2: Match a 2-D representation to a 3-D shape or structure.

In order to meet the benchmark, students' work should show that they can:

• Accurately match the Geoblock to the matching footprint.

Watching and talking with students as they complete the assessment will also provide information about **Benchmark 1:** Attend to features of 3-D shapes, such as overall size and shape, the number and shape of faces, and the number of corners.

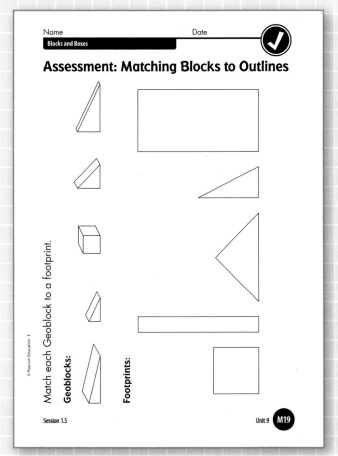

▲ Resource Masters, M19

(The Geoblock letters are provided for reference on the sample student work in this Teacher Note.)

Meeting the Benchmark

Students who meet the benchmark draw a line from each Geoblock picture to the footprint that matches it.

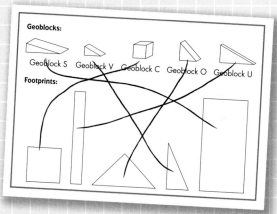

Sample Student Work

Students who need to use actual Geoblocks also fall into this category if they can select the correct blocks and place them on the proper outlines. Encourage these students to try to predict which outline will match the block *before* they place the block on the outline to test it.

Partially Meeting the Benchmark

Students in this category make one or two errors. Much of the work that led up to this assessment focused on the idea that one block could have more than one footprint. Therefore, a common mistake is for students to connect one block to more than one outline.

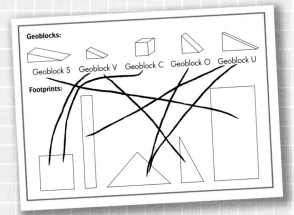

Sample Student Work

When these students have finished, explain that every outline on the sheet has a matching face somewhere on one of the blocks. Encourage them to find a block with a face that matches the one outline they have not yet used.

Another common error involves mixing up which triangular prisms go with the triangular footprints.

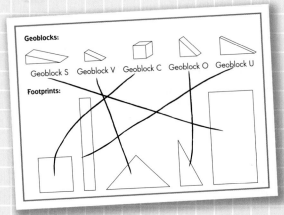

Sample Student Work

Ask these students about their work. If they do not find such errors on their own, ask them to find the actual Geoblocks that match the pictures and to show you how they fit on the outlines they chose. Encourage them to explain why they chose the matching blocks and outlines as pictured on the page, and how they could tell that they needed to change them when they used the actual blocks.

Not Meeting the Benchmark

Students in this category make more than two errors. Their errors may be similar in nature to those described above. You may also see some students who view the features of the pictures of the Geoblocks in a very general way. For example, Leah drew a line from Geoblock V to Outline 2. When asked about this choice, she said, "Well, look it has a rectangle. And this footprint is a rectangle."

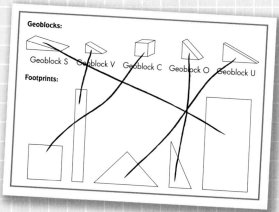

Leah's Work

Some students can attend to only one aspect of a given block or to the way it is oriented on the page. For example, a student may not see how the footprint for Geoblock U could be anything but a triangle, or may not be able to visualize a way to manipulate Geoblock V so that it would sit on Outline 4.

Make sure that these students are not making these errors because they are comparing 2-D pictures of 3-D shapes to 2-D outlines of some of the faces of those shapes. Ask these students to pick the pictured blocks out of a subset of Geoblocks and to think again about which block matches which outline. Again, encourage students to try to predict which outline will match the block *before* they place the block on the outline, but allow students who need to actually place the block on the outline to do so.

These students will benefit from more practice describing 3-D shapes, particularly their faces, with activities such as Geoblock Footprints from Session 1.1, page 26. Assign "Is It a Match?" *Student Activity Book* page 9 which provide tasks that are similar to this assessment.

Students Make Their Own Boxes

Students at this age level have a variety of approaches to making boxes out of flat pieces. Making a box requires visualizing how 2-D pieces can go together to make a 3-D shape, selecting pieces that fit together in the right way, and having enough manual dexterity to actually put the pieces together. Some students carefully lay out pieces flat on the table and can see how they will fold up when they are taped together to make a box. They put on the top after the rest is taped.

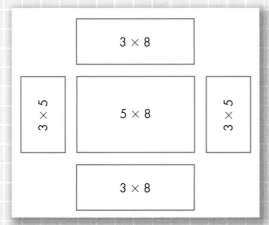

Some students who use this approach have difficulty finding the pieces that make a box. In the following example, five sides are placed in relationship to one another to make the bottom and sides of the box, but not all of the opposite sides match in size and shape. When taped together, one side will be smaller than the opposite side.

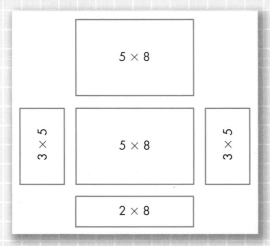

Expect students to make first attempts that do not work. Encourage them to find a way to fix the problem. Their approaches may include the following:

- Cutting off the side that does not work and replacing it with a piece of a different size

- Cutting a piece to attach onto the short side, making it closer in size to the opposite side

- Bending a 5″ × 8″ card to attach the short side to its opposite side, making a curved roof

Making a box is a complex task for young students. You do not need to insist that students make their boxes in the conventional manner if they solve the problems posed by this task in a reasonable way. For example, in one class, a first grader ignored the precut pieces and pieced together his own box by cutting pieces the sizes he wanted.

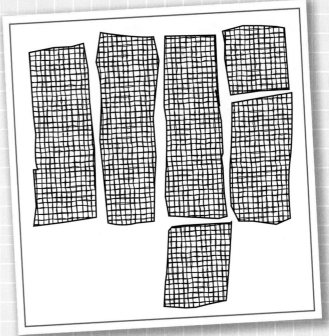

Teo's Work

Some students may begin with the precut pieces, and then cut their own pieces to finish the box. This is a common solution when students have taped together four sides, but find there is no piece that fits for the other two sides. For example, one first grade student attached four 3″ × 5″ cards together, but then had no 5″ × 5″ pieces for the top and bottom:

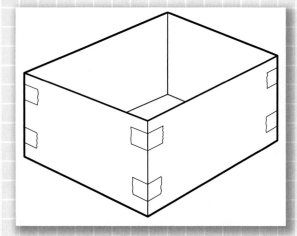

In this case, you can remind students that the pieces are like a puzzle and that they need to try a different combination of pieces if one way does not work. However, for some students, getting four sides together may have taken a great deal of work and attention. You may want to let them cut a top and bottom to fit, instead of asking them to start again.

During Session 1.7, some students make boxes using Box Pieces: Set B. One pair of students made four sides from 5″ × 8″ pieces, leaving an 8″ × 8″ opening at the top and bottom. There were no 8″ × 8″ pieces, so they experimented until they found that they could make an 8″ × 8″ piece by putting together a 5″ × 8″ and a 3″ × 8″ piece.

Some students may not be able to coordinate 2-D pieces to make a rectangular prism. These students may put pieces together to make some other 3-D object.

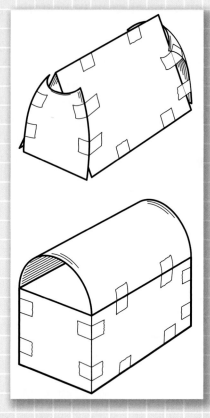

Expect a great deal of variation in the approaches your students use. At this age, differences in students' fine motor coordination will influence their work, as will their ability to visualize how 2-D pieces can go together to make a 3-D object. The goal of this activity is not for all students to construct boxes "correctly," but for all students to gain experience in visualizing and describing the components of rectangular prisms and in constructing 3-D objects from 2-D pieces. Students will have more experience with these ideas in the Grade 2 geometry unit *Shapes, Blocks, and Symmetry.*

Students Draw in 3-D

When most students first try to draw block constructions, they draw pictures that look two-dimensional. Many students draw the faces of blocks that they can see in one view of the building. Some carefully draw the shapes of these faces and arrange these "blocks" the way that they are arranged in the block construction. This is often a very effective way of showing all the blocks and how they are arranged.

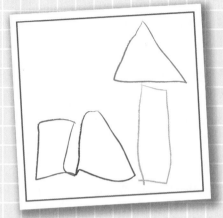

Seth's Work

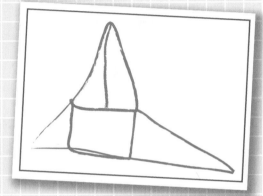

Diego's Work

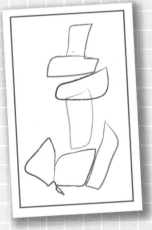

Emilia's Work      *Keena's Work*

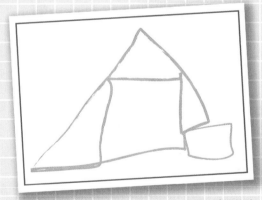

Paul's Work

Students vary in their ability to draw the shapes of the block faces that they see. Some are very careful to draw squares, rectangles, and triangles that are very close in shape to the faces of the blocks. Others have some difficulty drawing these shapes or showing how the blocks go together. Some may even show the outline of the whole construction without showing individual blocks.

Teachers can encourage these students to identify more carefully the shapes of the faces of the individual blocks and the way these blocks come together.

Many factors affect how well students can represent the constructions in drawings. Students' fine motor skills are developing in different ways, so some students are simply more skilled at or more interested in drawing than others. Another factor is students' care in observing the characteristics of the 3-D blocks.

The mathematics work in these sessions focuses on observing, describing, and comparing 3-D shapes. As you work with students, keep the emphasis on this careful observation and description, rather than on drawing skill. Ask questions such as these:

Which part of the block does this shape on your drawing show?

How were you looking at your building as you drew this? Where were you standing?

Which blocks does this triangular prism touch in the building? Is there a way you can show that on your drawing?

See **Dialogue Box:** Making It Look 3-D, page 121 for an example of how one teacher works with her students as they make drawings of block constructions.

Through experimenting and looking at one another's drawings, students will develop more ideas about how to make their drawings look 3-D, but you do not need to push students to do so. Let them see others' drawings and decide what techniques to try. One common method that students use is to draw adjacent faces of a block next to one another.

Sacha's Work

Sacha described her work as follows:

"I made the triangle first, and then I added two lines to make the rectangles. Then I made a cube. Then I made more rectangles to make the top and the sides."

This kind of drawing can very clearly show the blocks being used and their relationships to one another.

A closely related method is to draw a face of the block and then "surround" it with another outline of the same shape.

Neil's Work

Neil described his work as follows:

"See, first I drew it flat on the paper. Then to make it look three-dimensional, I drew the same shape next to it."

A more unusual approach for a first grader is the use of shading.

Felipe's Work

Despite the variety of skill levels, first graders in field-test classrooms enjoyed drawing block constructions and building from plans. It is important to keep these activities enjoyable by acknowledging how challenging they are for everyone and accepting the range of ways students represent their buildings. Through these activities, students become more aware of the different-shaped faces of 3-D objects and how these faces are connected to make a solid object.

End-of-Unit Assessment

Matching Plans to Buildings

Benchmark addressed:

Benchmark 2: Match a 2-D representation to a 3-D shape or structure.

In order to meet the benchmark, students' work should show that they can:

• Accurately match the 2-D drawings to the 3-D buildings.

Watching and talking with students as they complete this sheet will also provide information about **Benchmark 1:** Attend to features of 3-D shapes, such as overall size and shape, the number and shape of faces, and the number of corners.

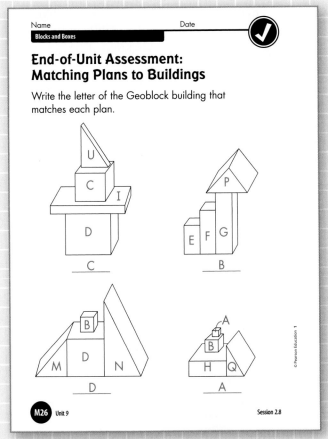

▲ **Resource Masters, M26**

Meeting the Benchmark

Students who meet the benchmark accurately match each building to its plan.

Not Meeting the Benchmark

Students in this category make errors as they try to match the plans to the buildings. They may say that one building matches more than one plan.

When these students have finished, explain that each drawing has its own building in the set of four. Encourage them to reconsider the plans and the buildings to see whether they can determine how each plan matches a different building.

Other students may be able to attend to only one aspect of a plan or a building or see the building in a very general way. For example, Lyle looked at the first outline and said, "Oh, it has a triangle on top." He then looked at the buildings and said, "Oh here it is!" and wrote B on the line beneath that picture.

Others may not be able to discern the relative size among the ramps in Buildings D and A and the difference among the other buildings. Encourage these students to take their time and to consider each building before they match it to a picture on the sheet. Have them show you specifically how the building they have chosen matches the plan, asking in particular about parts of the building the student seems not to have considered. See whether students can correct such mistakes on their own.

These students will benefit from more practice with activities such as Building and Drawing from Session 2.1, pages 72–73. You may want to give them 2-D plans and ask them to construct the buildings shown. At first, give them pictures of simple buildings made from two or three blocks that are quite different. Help them focus on one block at a time.

It Reminds Me Of . . .

This teacher begins the unit by showing students several different Geoblocks and asking for comments. Notice the features of 3-D shapes that students comment on and the language that they use.

Geoblock D   Geoblock K   Geoblock I

Teacher: Who can say something about this Geoblock? [D, a cube]

Sacha: It's a square shape.

Teo: It's a 3-D shape.

Jacob: It's a cube.

Stacy: It has eight points.

Vic: It looks like a box.

Talisa: Like a sugar cube.

Bruce: It's like my little sister's alphabet blocks.

Teacher: Here's another shape. [Geoblock K, the largest rectangular prism] What do you notice?

Libby: It has squares.

Teacher: What else do you see?

Felipe: Rectangles.

Toshi: It's a long box.

Lyle: It could be the side of a building.

Deshawn: It could be a mailbox.

Chris: It could be a milk carton.

Emilia: A tissue box.

Tamika: A washing machine.

Carol: A treasure chest.

The teacher asks Danielle to choose a shape. She chooses Geoblock I, a flat rectangular prism.

Diego: A book.

Nicky: It's a rectangle.

Leah: A really thin rectangle.

William: If you're going to buy a watch or a pen, this is like the box it comes in.

Paula: It's like a piece of mail.

Jacinta: The chalkboard.

Felipe: A picture frame.

Paul: It has eight corners, just like the last one.

When asked to describe a three-dimensional Geoblock, students comment on the overall size and shape of the block, the shape of its faces, and familiar objects that have the same shape. They use a wide range of geometric language (e.g., *square, cube, point, box, rectangle, long, thin, corner,* and so on) to describe and compare the shapes. This kind of conversation gives the teacher a sense of her students' experience with 3-D shapes and helps her plan ways to connect the content of this unit to what they already know.

Students compare Geoblocks to everyday objects.

Comparing Blocks to Pictures

Students have been trying to find the actual blocks pictured in the photographs on Geoblock Pictures: Sheet A (M9). As the teacher facilitates a discussion about the blocks students chose, she asks them to talk about and compare blocks that do not match as well as blocks that do.

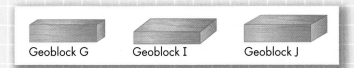

Geoblock G   Geoblock I   Geoblock J

Teacher: Let's start with this one. Hold up the block that you think matches the first picture.

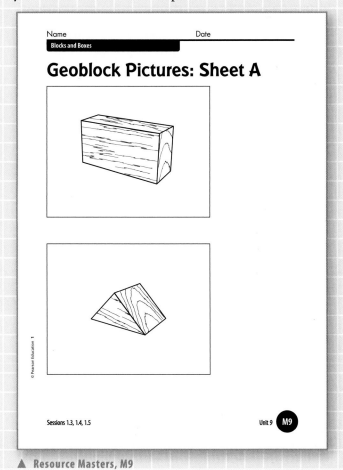

▲ Resource Masters, M9

Students hold up the blocks that they chose.

Teacher: I see a few different blocks. How did you decide which block best matched the picture?

Neil: It's thin. You can see that it's real thin on the ends.

Talisa: It has rectangles.

Teacher: So it has rectangles and it's thin on the ends. Did anyone have a block that you thought was right at first, but then you changed your mind?

Marta: I thought it might be this one [holds up Geoblock G]. See, it's kind of thin, too. But then I noticed that it has squares on the ends and this one doesn't have squares.

Teacher: That's a good observation. Does anyone else have a block that they think works for this picture or a reason why a block doesn't work?

Allie: At first, we picked up this one [holds up Geoblock I] because it's kind of long, but now we don't think it works.

Teacher: Why did you change your mind?

Allie shrugs. The teacher then holds Allie's block (Geoblock I) next to Geoblock J, the block many children held up as the match for the photograph.

Teacher: Who can help out? What can you say about these two blocks? Is there a way they're the same? Is there a way they're different?

Chris: They are kind of the same this way.

Chris holds the blocks together and shows how the longest dimensions are the same on both.

Teacher: It's kind of like footprints.

She holds them on the overhead so that the 4×8 side on each block is projected.

Teacher: If you look at them this way, they have the same footprint. Is there a way they're different?

Danielle: If you look at it another way, it's much thinner.

The teacher shows the 1×8 face of Geoblock I and the 2×8 face of Geoblock J on the overhead.

Teacher: So if you look at them this way, they look quite different. That's what Neil was saying before. Allie, does that have anything to do with why you changed your idea about which block works?

Allie: Yeah. That one's too thin.

This teacher encourages students to carefully compare the block they have chosen with the block in the photograph and with other blocks that are similar in some way. By asking them to explain why a block does or does not match the block in the photograph, the teacher helps students focus on important attributes of 3-D shapes.

Baby Shoes and Birdhouses

This class is discussing what the Mystery Boxes might be before some of them are revealed. The teacher holds up a large box that is about 12 in. × 8 in. × 3 in.

Bruce: It's cereal. I'm positive. It's exactly like my mom's box of cornflakes.

Seth: I think it's cereal, too. It couldn't be like a shoebox or something because it's tall like that and it's skinnier.

Libby: But it could be something like maybe a box that had some blocks or some building toys because I have a box like that, and it has blocks in it.

Teacher: Any more ideas? OK, let's unwrap it. (It is a cereal box.) You had great ideas about this box. You were really thinking about its size and shape. Paula, would you choose another box for us to unwrap?

Paula chooses a box that is about 9 in. × 4 in. × 4 in. Through the paper, it appears to have a top that fits on one of the 9″ × 4″ faces.

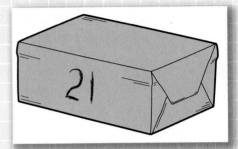

Sacha: Baby shoes. Because it's small and has a top on it.

Teo: I agree with Sacha because when my little sister got a pair, they came in a box like this.

The teacher asks Neil to unwrap it. It has a shoe brand name on it. Students call out, "Shoe box!"

Teacher: We'll do one more now. Then, if you want to, we can pick a few more while we're waiting for them to call the buses at the end of the day.

The teacher chooses a house-shaped box: a rectangular prism with a triangular prism on top of it, like a roof.

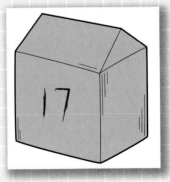

Stacy: A birdhouse.

Teacher: Why do you think so?

Stacy: Because it looks like one.

Teacher: What makes it look like one?

Stacy: The pointy end.

Neil: A doughnut box. That's the kind my dad gets when he gets doughnuts.

Emilia: I know! It's a kids' meal. A hamburger box and fries. 'Cause it's like ones I had before. The pointy part is where the handle is so you can carry it.

Teacher: Shall we unwrap it now? [Students shout, "Yes!"] Do you remember who brought this box in? Keena? [Keena unwraps the box.]

Various students: Animal crackers! We never guessed it!

As students try to guess what the Mystery Boxes held, they are paying attention to the size and shape of the boxes and relating that information to their function. For example, a small rectangular prism with a top probably held baby shoes. A box with a triangular or pointy top probably has a handle so that people can carry it easily.

Dialogue Box

Making It Look 3-D

These first-grade students are trying for the first time to make a drawing of their own block construction. Buildings were limited to three or four blocks. The teacher circulates and interacts with students as they work, asking them to show how their drawings match the blocks and encouraging them to experiment and revise.

Leah has drawn the front triangular face of a triangular prism, but now she is frowning and tapping her pencil on the table.

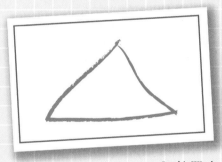

Leah's Work

Teacher: I can see that your drawing shows this triangular prism, but you don't seem satisfied.

Leah: It doesn't show this part [points to the top edge of the block].

Teacher: Is there some way you want to try to revise your drawing?

Leah: I'll put in some more lines.

Leah changes her drawing to look like this:

Leah's Work

Diego is working on a taller, stacked building.

Block Building

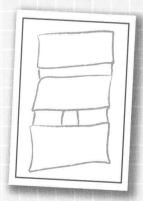

Diego's Work

Teacher: It's really interesting how you drew this. How were you looking at your building?

Diego: I was looking from the top. See, they all have squares on top and these little skinny parts are the spaces between the blocks.

Teacher: Can you show me where you see this in your building?

The teacher points to the small square in Diego's drawing.

Diego: Here [points to the top of the small, rectangular prism].

Teacher: So this square represents the top of this block. What does this part of your drawing represent?

The teacher then asks Diego to show her which blocks other parts of the drawing represent.

Teacher: So when you drew your building, you were looking down on it from above. Sometimes people call that a bird's eye view. What if you look at your building from your seat?

The teacher kneels next to Diego, and together they look at the building from that view.

Teacher: How does the bottom block look from this view?

Diego: A long rectangle.

Teacher: You see a long rectangle on the bottom. Why don't you try *another* drawing of your building, but this time draw it from the side? It will be interesting to compare the two drawings when you're done!

Drawing a three-dimensional structure in two dimensions is a challenging task. Each structure is made up of several Geoblocks, and each Geoblock has multiple features. For example, a triangular prism has one face that is a triangle but other faces that are rectangles. It may be small, medium, or large; thick or thin; and equilateral or not. Students must see the 2-D shapes on a block and how they fit together to make one 3-D shape, see how several blocks are arranged in relation to one another, and find a way to show that on a two-dimensional piece of paper. In addition, there are many ways to view one building. Four students drawing the same structure from different seats are likely to have different final products. Notice how this teacher encourages Diego to consider this fact and to experiment with drawing the same building from a different perspective.

Dialogue Box

Arcades, Parks, and Hardware Stores

This class is brainstorming what buildings they need in their class town. The following is their list so far:

school	houses
apartment buildings	candy and toy store
skating rink and arcade	library
grocery store	

Teacher: You said you needed both houses and apartment buildings. Why?

Felipe: Because a lot of us live in apartment buildings and some of us live in houses.

Teacher: OK. Who can explain what an arcade is?

Jacinta: It has lots of stores and you can buy fun things there.

Teacher: Is the skating rink in the arcade?

William: It can be.

Teacher: Imagine that this is your town. What else would you need?

Talisa: You need roads and cars.

Teacher: Roads and cars aren't buildings, so I'm going to start a second list for things that aren't buildings.

She starts another list labeled, "Other things we need."

Jacob: Parks.

Teacher: Why do you need parks?

Jacob: I don't know.

Sacha: So you can go and play if you don't have a yard.

Teacher: I'll put parks with roads and cars on the second list. We can decide which of the areas on our street grid should be parks.

Carol: We should put Burger Hut.

Teacher: What kind of store is that?

Carol: A food store.

Teacher: Well, we have a grocery store. That's a food store. Is this something different?

Teo: The food is cooked.

Bruce: You eat right there.

Marta: It's a restaurant.

The teacher adds *restaurant* to the list.

Diego: I know. A supermarket.

Teacher: Is that a different kind of food store?

Emilia: We have grocery store. It's the same thing.

Tamika: No, a supermarket's bigger than a grocery store.

Teacher: Do you think so? I'll put supermarket next to grocery store. Any other ideas of what we need?

Chris: We should put F & S. Cause you need things to fix up all the buildings.

Teacher: What kind of store is F & S?

Chris: Where you get stuff, nails, hammers, boards. . .

Nicky: A hardware store.

This discussion gives students an opportunity to think about the range of buildings in a community, what they are called, and what purpose they serve.

The *Student Math Handbook* pages related to this unit are pictured on the following pages. This book is designed to be used flexibly: as a resource for students doing classwork, as a book students can take home for reference while doing homework and playing math games with their families, and as a reference for families to better understand the work their children are doing in class.

When students take the *Student Math Handbook* home, they and their families can discuss these pages together to reinforce or enhance students' understanding of the mathematical concepts and games in this unit.

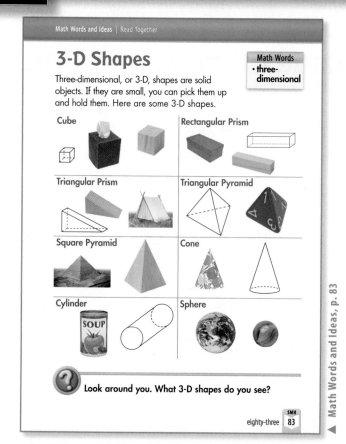

◄ Math Words and Ideas, p. 83

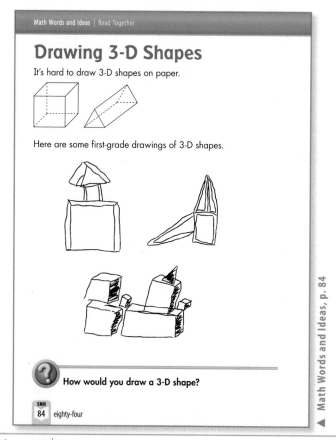

◄ Math Words and Ideas, p. 84

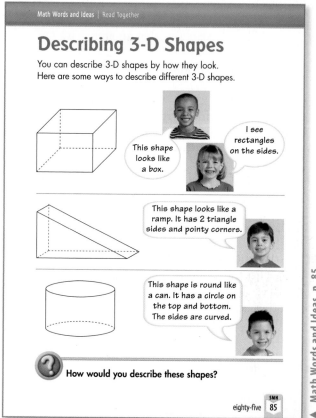

◄ Math Words and Ideas, p. 85

Describing 3-D Shapes: Edges, Faces, and Vertices (Corners)

Math Words
- edges
- faces

3-D shapes have faces, edges, and vertices. Think about a cube.

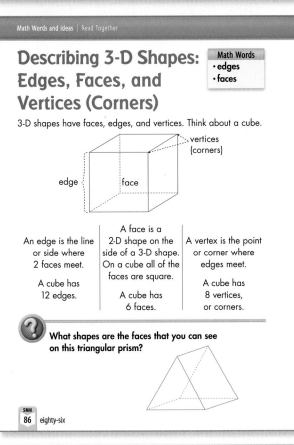

An edge is the line or side where 2 faces meet. A cube has 12 edges.	A face is a 2-D shape on the side of a 3-D shape. On a cube all of the faces are square. A cube has 6 faces.	A vertex is the point or corner where edges meet. A cube has 8 vertices, or corners.

? **What shapes are the faces that you can see on this triangular prism?**

SMH **86** eighty-six

◄ Math Words and Ideas, p. 86

Naming 3-D Shapes: Prisms

Math Words
- prism
- rectangular prism
- triangular prism
- cube

A prism is a 3-D shape that has only flat faces. These prisms have 2 opposite faces that are the same. These faces are connected by rectangles.

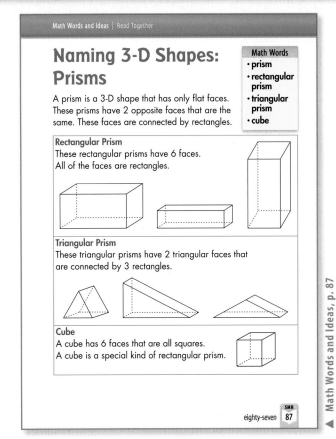

Rectangular Prism
These rectangular prisms have 6 faces. All of the faces are rectangles.

Triangular Prism
These triangular prisms have 2 triangular faces that are connected by 3 rectangles.

Cube
A cube has 6 faces that are all squares. A cube is a special kind of rectangular prism.

eighty-seven SMH **87**

◄ Math Words and Ideas, p. 87

Naming 3-D Shapes

Math Words
- pyramid
- cylinder
- sphere
- cone

Here are some other 3-D shapes.

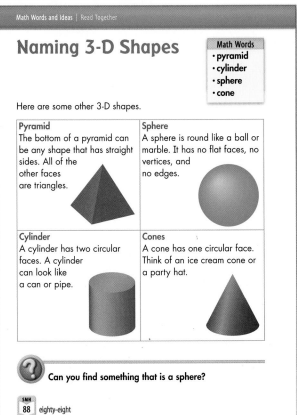

Pyramid The bottom of a pyramid can be any shape that has straight sides. All of the other faces are triangles.	**Sphere** A sphere is round like a ball or marble. It has no flat faces, no vertices, and no edges.
Cylinder A cylinder has two circular faces. A cylinder can look like a can or pipe.	**Cones** A cone has one circular face. Think of an ice cream cone or a party hat.

? **Can you find something that is a sphere?**

SMH **88** eighty-eight

◄ Math Words and Ideas, p. 88

Footprints

Math Words
- footprint

A footprint is an outline of a foot. Different shaped feet make different kinds of footprints.

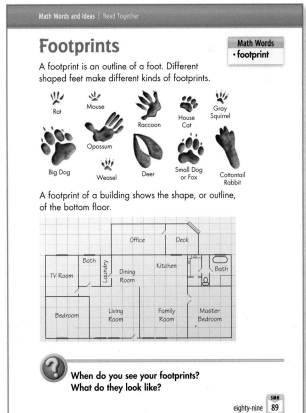

Rat Mouse Raccoon House Cat Gray Squirrel

Big Dog Opossum Weasel Deer Small Dog or Fox Cottontail Rabbit

A footprint of a building shows the shape, or outline, of the bottom floor.

Office Deck
Bath Kitchen Bath
TV Room Laundry Dining Room
Bedroom Living Room Family Room Master Bedroom

? **When do you see your footprints? What do they look like?**

eighty-nine SMH **89**

◄ Math Words and Ideas, p. 89

Geoblock Footprints

A footprint of a Geoblock is an outline of one of its faces. The same block can have several different footprints, depending on which way it is turned.

For example, this triangular prism has 3 footprints.

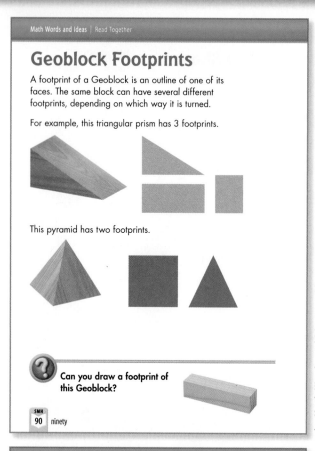

This pyramid has two footprints.

? **Can you draw a footprint of this Geoblock?**

SMH
90 ninety

▲ Math Words and Ideas, p. 90

Building with 3-D Shapes

These first graders made a town with 3-D shapes. They also drew 2-D plans of all the buildings in the town. A 2-D plan helps people build the right 3-D building. It can also help them fix the building if it falls down.

Here are some examples of 2-D plans and 3-D buildings:

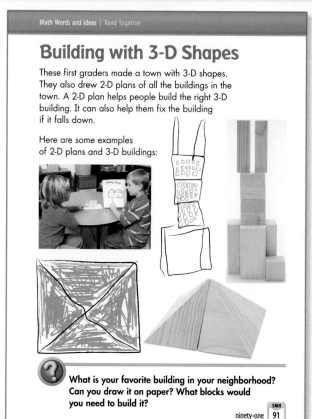

? **What is your favorite building in your neighborhood? Can you draw it on paper? What blocks would you need to build it?**

ninety-one
SMH
91

▲ Math Words and Ideas, p. 91

Giving Directions

Some first graders made a block town in their classroom. Here is a map of their town.

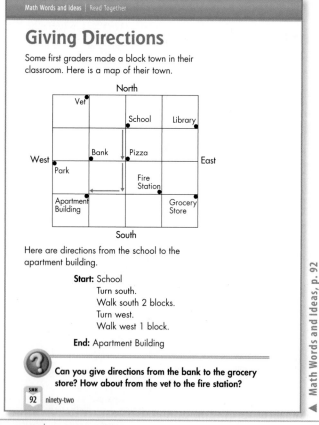

Here are directions from the school to the apartment building.

Start: School
Turn south.
Walk south 2 blocks.
Turn west.
Walk west 1 block.

End: Apartment Building

? **Can you give directions from the bank to the grocery store? How about from the vet to the fire station?**

SMH
92 ninety-two

▲ Math Words and Ideas, p. 92

Index

IN THIS UNIT